Ready® | 7

Mathematics
PRACTICE AND
PROBLEM SOLVING

SO-AFU-973

Vice President-Product Development: Adam Berkin
Editorial Director: Cynthia Tripp
Editorial: Stacie Cartwright, Pam Halloran, Kathy Kellman, Lauren Van Wart
Project Manager: Grace Izzi
Cover Designer and Illustrator: Matt Pollock
Illustrator: Sam Valentino
Photography Credit: wk1003mike/Shutterstock (front cover background)

NOT FOR RESALE

ISBN 978-1-4957-0484-0
©2016—Curriculum Associates, LLC
North Billerica, MA 01862

30 29 28 27 26 25 24 23 22 21 20

BTS22

802385

Table of Contents

Family Letter available with every lesson.

Table of Contents

Family Letter available with every lesson.

iv

Dear Family,

Your child is learning to understand how to add positive and negative integers.

All of the whole numbers and their opposites are called integers. The numbers 4, −8, 21, −17, 158, and −1,000 are examples of integers. Integers are used to represent quantities in real-life situations that involve positive and negative numbers. Here are some examples of situations in which you might use integers:

- to describe whole-dollar deposits and withdrawals in a bank account

- to represent elevations above or below sea level

- to describe stock market gains and losses

- to report temperatures above and below 0 degrees

Just like you can add whole numbers, you can also add integers. If you add an integer to its opposite, the sum is 0. For example, 4 and −4 are opposites.

$$4 + (-4) = 0 \qquad (-4) + 4 = 0$$

Opposites like 4 and −4 are said to be *additive inverses* because their sum is 0. Any two numbers whose sum is 0 are additive inverses.

Consider this situation:

A fisherman is fishing on a bridge that is 3 feet above the surface of a river. The bottom of the river is 12 feet below the bridge. What is the position of the bottom of the river relative to the surface of the water?

The next page shows two different ways your child may use integer addition to find the position of the bottom of the river relative to the surface of the water.

A fisherman is fishing on a bridge that is 3 feet above the surface of a river. The bottom of the river is 12 feet below the bridge. What is the position of the bottom of the river relative to the surface of the water?

To find the position of the bottom of the river relative to the surface of the water, you need to add −12 to 3.

One way:
Use a number line to add.

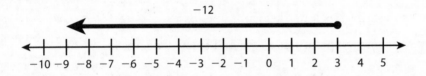

$$3 + (-12) = -9$$

Another way:
Break apart, or decompose, numbers to form additive inverses.

You can think of −12 as (−3) + (−9).

$$3 + (-12) = 3 + (-3) + (-9)$$
$$= [3 + (-3)] + (-9)$$
$$= 0 + (-9)$$
$$= -9$$

Answer: Both methods show that adding −12 to 3 gives a sum of −9, so the bottom of the river is −9 feet from the surface of the river.

Understand
Addition of Positive and Negative Integers

Name: _____

Prerequisite: **What is the absolute value of a number?**

Study the example showing how to find the absolute value of a number. Then solve problems 1–10.

Example

The *absolute value* of a number is the distance from the number to 0 on a number line. Both −4 and 4 are 4 units from 0, so |−4| = 4 and |4| = 4.

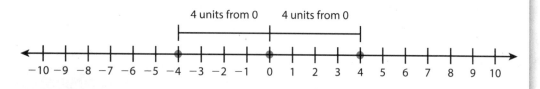

1 What is the absolute value of 0? _____

Use the number line to solve problems 2–4.

2 Graph the numbers 6, 0, −10, 9, and −6 on the number line.

3 Which number that you graphed has the greatest absolute value? What is the absolute value of that number? _____

4 Which two numbers that you graphed have the same absolute value? Explain.

_____

5 Write <, =, or > to compare the numbers.

   a. −7 ☐ −1   **d.** |0| ☐ |−1|

   b. |−7| ☐ |−1| **e.** 12 ☐ |12|

   c. 0 ☐ −1   **f.** −12 ☐ −|12|

Vocabulary

absolute value the distance a number is from 0 on the number line.

|2| = 2 |−3| = 3

Solve.

The table shows information about each of the Great Lakes. It shows the elevation of the surface of each lake and the elevation of the deepest point of each lake, both relative to sea level.

	Surface Level (ft)	Deepest Point (ft)
Lake Superior	601	−732
Lake Michigan	577	−346
Lake Ontario	243	−559
Lake Huron	577	−173
Lake Erie	569	210

6 Show the surface levels and deepest points from the table on the number line.

7 Which number in the table has the greatest absolute value? What is the absolute value of that number?

_____

8 Which of the Great Lakes, if any, is entirely above sea level? Explain.

_____

_____

0 ┼─ Sea Level

9 How can you use absolute value to find the distance from the surface of Lake Michigan to its deepest point? What is the distance?

_____

_____

_____

_____

10 The deepest point of Lake Titicaca in South America is −922 feet relative to its surface. The deepest point is 11,542 feet above sea level. What is the elevation of the surface of the lake? Use absolute value to explain.

_____

_____

Lesson 1 *Understand* Addition of Positive and Negative Integers

Add Positive and Negative Integers

Study the example problem showing how to add positive and negative integers. Then solve problems 1–8.

Example

Graph each situation on a number line. Then, model each situation with an equation.

- Jordan already owes $5 to Kiara and borrows $4 from Don. How much money does Jordan have?

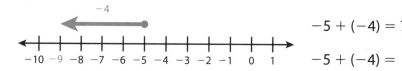

$$-5 + (-4) = ?$$
$$-5 + (-4) = -9$$

- Micah has $4 and owes Ben $7.

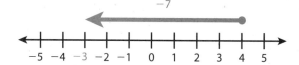

$$4 + (-7) = ?$$
$$4 + (-7) = -3$$

---

1 Complete the equation and model each sum on a number line.

a.  $+ 4 = 0$

b. $-5 +$  $= 0$

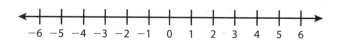

c. When will the sum of two numbers be zero?

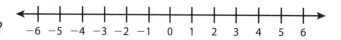

_____

_____

2 In the first box of each equation, write an example of an integer that will result in the sum described. Then write the sum. Model each sum on a number line.

a. positive sum: $-5 +$ 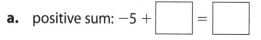 $=$ ☐

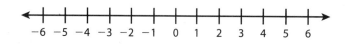

b. negative sum: $-4 +$ 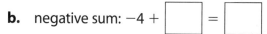 $=$ ☐

Lesson 1 *Understand* Addition of Positive and Negative Integers

Solve.

3 Explain how you can use absolute value to tell whether the sum of two integers is positive or negative.

_____

_____

_____

4 An elevator is two floors below ground level and goes up 5 floors. Write an addition equation that models the location of the elevator relative to ground level. What integer represents the new location?

_____

5 One morning, the temperature was −5°F. By noon, the temperature had increased 12 degrees. What was the temperature at noon? Use a model to explain your answer.

_____

6 A lobster fisherman moves a lobster trap from 20 feet below sea level to a location that is 15 feet deeper. Draw a number line and write an addition equation that models this situation. What integer represents the new location relative to sea level?

_____

7 The sum of integers p and q is modeled on a number line, where $|p| < |q|$. In each box, write p, q, or $p + q$. Then write an addition equation using integers that could represent p, q, and $p + q$.

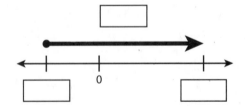

_____

8 Show how the model in problem 7 would change if $|p| > |q|$. Draw the model, labeling p, q, and $p + q$. Then write an addition equation using integers that could represent p, q, and $p + q$.

_____

Name: _____

Reason and Write

Study the example. Underline two parts that you think make it a particularly good answer and a helpful example.

Example

You are designing a hike that starts at the bottom of a small mountain, below sea level. You plan to stop at three locations:

- a scenic location, which is below sea level

- a picnic area for lunch, which is at sea level

- the top of the mountain, which is 800 feet above sea level

Design the hike. Choose the location of each stop. Make a table that shows each location, the change in elevation from the previous location, and the elevation of each location relative to sea level. Show how you found the elevation of each location using integer addition. Graph your locations on a number line. Describe your hike, including the total change in elevation from the start of the hike to the mountaintop.

Show your work. Use integers, tables, models, equations, and words to explain your answer.

Where does the example . . .

- use integers?

- use a table and a number line?

- use an equation to model?

- use words to explain?

- answer the question?

Elevation (feet)

Location	Change in Elevation	New Elevation
Start		−200
Scenic location	150	−50
Lunch	50	0
Mountaintop	800	800

Addition of integers also shows the elevation at each location and the total change in elevation.

$$-200 + 150 = -50$$
$$-50 + 50 = 0$$
$$0 + 800 = 800$$

Total change: $800 + 50 + 150 = 1,000$

Starting at –200 feet and climbing 150 feet will bring me to an elevation of –50 feet. After climbing another 50 feet, I will be at sea level, or an elevation of 0 feet. Finally, climbing the final 800 feet will bring me to the mountaintop at an elevation of 800 feet. The total change in elevation will be 1,000 feet.

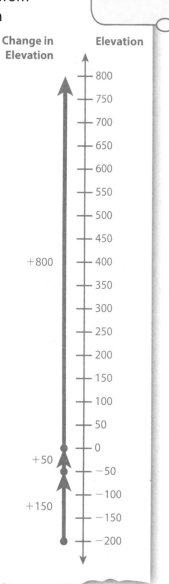

Solve the problem. Use what you learned from the model.

You are designing a hike that starts at the top of a canyon, above sea level. You plan to stop at three locations:

- a scenic landmark, which is at sea level

- a famous boulder, which is below sea level

- the bottom of the canyon, which is 600 feet below sea level

Design the hike. Choose the location of each stop. Make a table that shows each location, the change in elevation from the previous location, and the elevation of each location relative to sea level. Show how you found the elevation of each location using integer addition. Graph your locations on a number line. Describe your hike, including the total change in elevation from the start of the hike to the bottom of the canyon.

Did you . . .
- use integers?
- use a table and a number line?
- use an equation to model?
- use words to explain?
- answer the question?

Show your work. Use integers, tables, models, equations, and words to explain your answer.

Dear Family,

Your child is learning to understand how to subtract positive and negative integers.

Addition and subtraction are inverse operations. You can write any subtraction problem as an addition problem. Here's an example:

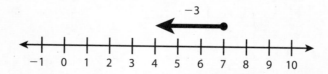

Subtraction problem:　　7　　−　　3　　=　　4　⎫
　　　　　　　　　　　　　　　　　　　　　　　　　⎬ same result
Addition problem:　　　7　　+　　(−3)　　=　　4　⎭

Keep the same first number.　　　　　Use the opposite of
　　　　　　　　　　　　　　　　　　the second number.

　　　　　　Use the inverse operation.

This means that if you know how to add positive and negative integers, you know how to subtract them.

$$-3$$

```
←——————————————————————→
 −1  0  1  2  3  4  5  6  7  8  9  10
```

Consider the following example:

The temperature is −1°F at noon. In the evening, the temperature is −3°F. What is the difference in the temperatures?

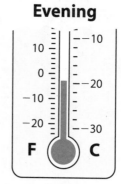

On the next page you will see a way your child may find the difference in the temperatures.

The temperature is −1°F at noon. In the evening, the temperature is −3°F. What is the difference in the temperatures?

Write a subtraction problem and use a number line to model an equivalent addition problem.

To do this, keep the first number the same, change subtraction to addition, and add the opposite of the second number. You can do this because subtracting a number is the same as adding its opposite.

$$-1 - (-3) = -1 + 3$$

Now you can use a number line to find the sum.

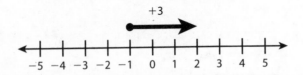

Solve the addition problem: $-1 + 3 = 2$.

Answer: The result is 2, meaning that the difference between the temperature of −1°F at noon and −3°F in the evening is 2°F.

Understand
Subtraction of Positive and Negative Integers

Name: _____

Prerequisite: How do you add integers using a number line?

Study the example problem showing how to add positive and negative integers. Then solve problems 1–7.

Example

When Leo woke up he saw that the temperature was −8°F. By noon the temperature had increased 5°F. What was the temperature at noon?

You can use a number line to add −8 + 5.

−8 + 5 = −3, so the temperature at noon was −3°F.

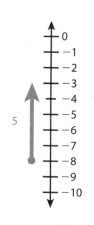

1   By 3:00 PM, the temperature had increased by another 5°F. Was the temperature at 3:00 PM positive or negative? How do you know? What was the temperature at 3:00 PM?

_____

_____

2   By 11:00 PM, the temperature had dropped 8°F. Was the temperature at 11:00 PM positive or negative? Explain.

_____

_____

3   A swimmer dives 10 feet below the surface of a lake. How far must she swim before she reaches the surface? Use an addition equation to explain, and tell what each part of the equation means.

_____

_____

Solve.

4 Use a number line to show $4 + (-7)$. Then complete the equation that shows the sum.

$4 + (-7) = $ _____

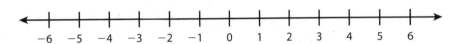

5 In a game that you are playing, your friend says that she has −6 points "give or take" 4 points. You currently have −3 points in the game. Can you say who is winning? Why or why not? Use a number line to explain.

_____

_____

6 Leon used the number line below to show $-5 + 4$. Explain what is wrong with his model.

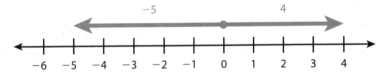

_____

_____

7 The sum of two integers is –4.

a. Can the two integers both be positive? Explain.

_____

_____

b. Can the two integers both be negative? Explain.

_____

_____

Name: _____

Subtract Positive and Negative Integers

Study the example problem showing how to subtract two integers. Then solve problems 1–4.

Example

What is the difference between an elevation of −4 feet and an elevation of 8 feet?

Find the difference by subtracting: $8 - (-4)$.
Write the subtraction as an addition problem: $8 + 4$.

Model the addition problem on a number line.

The difference in the elevations is 12 feet.

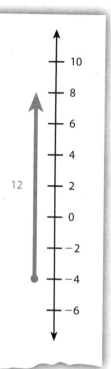

1 Marcie is playing a board game with a friend. She needs 20 points to win. She currently has −10 points. She wants to know the difference between the number of points she now has and the number of points she needs.

a. Write a subtraction problem to represent the situation. Then write the subtraction problem as an addition problem.

_____

b. Model the addition problem on the number line.

c. What is the difference between the number of points she needs to win and the number of points she now has?

_____

Solve.

2 Jessie uses the number line below to help write
$-2 + (-4)$ as a subtraction problem.

a. What is wrong with Jessie's number line?

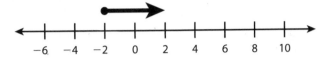

_____

b. Write the subtraction problem and the answer.

_____

3 Use the number line below to solve the problems.

a. What is the distance between -5 and -1 on the
number line? _____

b. What is $|-5 - (-1)|$? _____

c. What do you notice about the absolute value of the
difference between the two numbers?

_____

4 What number must be subtracted from -5 for the
difference to be -2? Explain your answer. Include a
number line in your explanation.

_____

_____

_____

_____

Name: _____

Study the example. Underline two parts that you think make it a particularly good answer and a helpful example.

Example

You and your friends Aaron, Beth, and Craig all live on the same street that the school is on. Aaron lives farthest from the school. You and Aaron live the same distance from Beth's house. Craig lives closest to the school.

Place points A for Aaron's house, B for Beth's house, C for Craig's house, and S for the school on a number line. Let your house X be at 0. Describe each person's location and use absolute value to find the distance that each person has to walk to and from school. Then, list the locations in order from farthest from the school to closest to the school.

Show your work. Use the number line, words, absolute value, and equations to explain your answer.

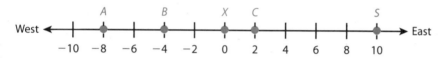

Aaron's house is located at −8 on my number line, and the school is at 10. So his distance from school is: $|10 - (-8)| = |18| = 18$ units. He has to walk $2(18) = 36$ units to and from school each day.

Beth's house is located at −4 on my number line, and the school is at 10. So her distance from school is: $|10 - (-4)| = |14| = 14$ units. She has to walk $2(14) = 28$ units to and from school each day.

My house is located at 0 on my number line, and the school is at 10. So my distance from school is: $|10 - 0| = |10| = 10$ units. I have to walk $2(10) = 20$ units to and from school each day.

Craig's house is located at 2 on my number line, and the school is at 10. So his distance from school is: $|10 - 2| = |8| = 8$ units. He has to walk $2(8) = 16$ units to and from school each day.

In order from farthest to closest, the locations are Aaron's house, Beth's house, my house, Craig's house.

Where does the example . . .

• use the number line?

• use words?

• use absolute value?

• use equations?

• answer each part of the problem?

Solve the problem. Use what you learned from the model.

You and your friends Ari, Ben, and Carla all live on the same street that some tennis courts are on. Ari and Carla live the same distance from the tennis courts. Ben lives farthest from the courts. You live the same distance from Ben's house and the tennis courts.

Place points *A* for Ari's house, *B* for Ben's house, *C* for Carla's house, and *T* for the tennis courts on a number line. Let your house *X* be at 0. Describe each person's location and use absolute value to find the distance that each person has to walk to and back home from the tennis courts. Then, list the locations in order from farthest from the courts to closest to the courts.

Show your work. Use the number line, words, absolute value, and equations to explain your answer.

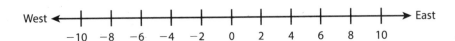

Did you . . .

- use the number line?
- use words?
- use absolute value?
- use equations?
- answer each part of the problem?

Dear Family,

Your child is learning about adding and subtracting positive and negative integers.

You can use positive and negative integers to represent real-world amounts. For example, a real-world situation that involves adding positive and negative integers is making deposits to and withdrawals from a bank account.

Another real-world situation that involves subtracting positive and negative integers is finding the difference between two elevations. For example, suppose you want to find the difference between the elevation of a mountain that is 2,000 feet above sea level and the elevation of a valley that is 500 feet below sea level.

Use a subtraction equation to find the difference between the elevations.

- Represent the mountain elevation with an integer: +2,000
- Represent the valley elevation with an integer: −500

$$2,000 - (-500) = 2,000 + 500$$
$$= 2,500$$

The difference means that there are 2,500 feet between the mountain's elevation of 2,000 feet and the valley's elevation of −500 feet.

Consider this situation:

Emily has a score of −5 points in the video game she is playing. She scores 12 points during her next turn. How many points does she have now?

The next page shows two different ways your child may use to add positive and negative numbers to find the number of points Emily has now.

NEXT

Lesson 3 Add and Subtract Positive and Negative Integers   **17**

Emily has a score of −5 points in the video game she is playing. She scores 12 points during her next turn. How many points does she have now?

To find Emily's point total, you need to add −5 and 12.

One way:
Use a number line.

Start at −5. Move 12 units to the right.

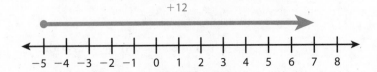

End at 7.

A second way:
Use an equation.

The model shows words that represent the situation.
Use the model to write and solve an equation.

Points Emily starts with	+	Points she earns	=	Points she has now
−5	+	12	=	7

Answer: Both methods show that the sum of −5 and 12 is 7. This means that Emily has 7 points now.

Add and Subtract Positive and Negative Integers

Name: _____

Prerequisite: Connect Addition and Subtraction

Study the example showing how to connect addition and subtraction. Then solve problems 1–9.

Example

Solve the subtraction problem: $7 - 4 = \square$.

To solve, you can represent $7 - 4 = \square$ using a number line. Start at 7 and move 4 units to the left to represent subtracting 4 from 7. You end at 3, so $7 - 4 = 3$.

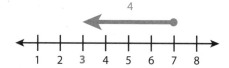

Because addition and subtraction are inverse operations, you can also rewrite the subtraction problem as an addition problem. Think: "What number do I add to 4 to get 7?" Because $4 + 3 = 7$, you know $7 - 4 = 3$.

1 Draw a number line that represents $7 + (-4)$.

2 How does the number line you drew in problem 1 compare to the number line in the example?

_____

3 Use your answers to the last two problems to complete this equation.

$7 - 4 = 7 +$ _____

4 Complete each equation.

a. $-1 + (-4) =$ _____ **c.** $-1 + (-4) = -1 -$ _____

b. $-1 -$ _____ $= -5$ **d.** $1 - (-4) = 1 + 4 =$ _____

Solve.

5 The average low temperature for one winter day is 10°F. The low temperature on that day was actually −2°F.

    a. Write a subtraction problem to represent the situation. Then write the subtraction problem as an addition problem.

    _____

    b. Model the addition problem on a number line.

    c. What is the difference in the temperatures?

    _____

6 Write an addition expression that is equivalent to $65 - 79$. Then evaluate the expression.

_____

7 Explain how to write any subtraction problem as an addition problem. Why does it help to write a subtraction problem as an addition problem?

_____

_____

_____

8 Write an absolute value expression to represent the distance between −1 and 6 on a number line. Then evaluate the expression.

_____

9 The expression $x - 4$ represents a negative integer. What integers could x represent?

_____

Name: _____

Addition Methods for Integers

Study the example problem showing how to add positive and negative integers. Then solve problems 1–7.

Example

At the end of the first round of a game, Luis has a score of −5 points. At the end of the second round, he has a score of 3 points. How many points did he score during the second round?

You can use a number line to help you understand the problem.

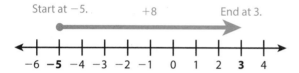

Start at −5.   +8   End at 3.

−6 **−5** −4 −3 −2 −1 0 1 2 **3** 4

The number line shows that Luis scored 8 points during the second round.

---

1 Complete this model to represent the problem.

score at the end
of first round   +   =

2 Write an addition equation using numbers to represent the verbal equation in problem 1.

_____

3 Amy said she would have solved this problem differently. She saw that she was looking for the difference between the score in the second round, 3, and the score in the first round, −5, so she wrote the expression 3 − (−5). Does her method work? Explain.

_____

_____

Lesson 3 Add and Subtract Positive and Negative Integers   **21**

Solve.

4 The temperature in Indianapolis was −4°F at 7:00 AM. The temperature rose 3°F by noon. What was the temperature at noon? Use a number line to find the answer.

_____

5 Aiden had saved $22 before he earned $25 mowing a lawn. He then spent $32 on a suitcase. How much money does he have now? Explain how you found your answer.

_____

6 Omar has a score of 12 in a bean-bag toss game. On his next turn he gets −8 points. Use the bar model to write an addition sentence that shows Omar's score now.

12	
?	8

_____

7 Gina works in a clothing store. At noon, she has $125 in the cash register. James gives her $60 for a sweater, and she gives him $7 change. Hana then gives her $40 for a blouse and receives $3 change. Use a series of addition equations to find out how much money Gina has in her cash register at the end of these sales.

Show your work.

Solution: _____

Name: _____

Subtraction Methods for Integers

Study the example showing how to subtract positive and negative integers. Then solve problems 1–4.

Example

Two friends are playing a game with a spinner that has positive and negative numbers on it. Each player takes turns spinning the spinner. The table shows the results of the first 4 rounds.

	Round 1	Round 2	Round 3	Round 4
Player 1	2	−5	−5	8
Player 2	12	−10	2	−4
Team Score				

The team score at the end of each round is found by subtracting Player 2's score from Player 1's score.

For Round 1: Subtracting 12 from 2 is the same as adding −12. Start at 2 and move left 12 units to arrive at −10.

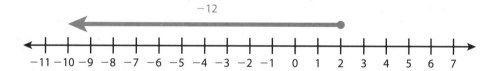

For Round 2: Subtracting −10 is the same as adding 10. Start at −5 and move right 10 units to arrive at 5.

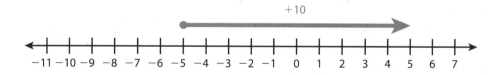

1 Use a number line to find the team score for Round 3.

Round 3 team score: _____

Solve.

2 Refer to the table from the previous page.

	Round 1	Round 2	Round 3	Round 4
Player 1	2	−5	−5	8
Player 2	12	−10	2	−4
Team Score				

On which round did the team get the highest score?
Explain your answer.

_____

_____

_____

3 Anita recorded the daily high and low temperatures as
13°F and −3°F, respectively.

a. Write the difference in temperatures, in °F, as a
subtraction equation. Then write the difference in
temperatures as an addition equation.

_____

b. Give an example of a positive temperature and a
negative temperature that have a difference of 5°F.

_____

4 Consider the following problems.

a. Write a subtraction equation that involves one
negative integer but results in a positive difference.
Does the other integer have to be positive?
Explain your answer.

_____

_____

b. Write a subtraction problem involving two positive
integers with a negative difference. Explain the
relationship between the two integers that must
exist for the difference to be negative.

_____

_____

Name: _____

Add and Subtract Positive and Negative Integers

Solve the problems.

1   The element bromine turns into a liquid at −7°C, and it turns into a gas at 59°C. From the temperature at which bromine becomes a liquid, by how many degrees must the temperature change for it to turn into a gas?

Should you add or subtract?

A	−66°C	**C**	52°C
B	−52°C	**D**	66°C

Johnathan chose **C** as his answer. How did he get that answer?

_____

2   Lamont keeps track of his math grades by recording them in a table. He wants to keep an average of 90, so he also lists the amount that each grade is above or below 90.

You may want to group the positive numbers and the negative numbers.

a.   Complete the table.

Test	1	2	3	4	5	6
Grade	83	94	79		96	
Above/Below 90	−7	4		7		−3

b.   Use the numbers in the *Above/Below 90* row to find out whether Lamont's average is above or below 90.

Show your work.

_____

_____

Solution: _____

c.   What grade does Lamont need to get on the next test to have an average of exactly 90? Explain your answer.

_____

_____

Solve.

3 Which expressions are equivalent to −9? Select all that are correct.

Recall how to write a subtraction problem as an addition problem.

   A $8 - 8 + 9$

   B $3 - (-6) + (-18)$

   C $-1 + 7 - (-3)$

   D $4 - 5 - 8$

---

4 Tell whether each equation is *True* or *False*.

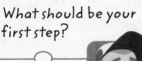

What should be your first step?

   a. $-4 + (-7) = 11$ ☐ True   ☐ False

   b. $5 + (-4) = -5 + 4$ ☐ True   ☐ False

   c. $-10 + 7 = 7 - 10$ ☐ True   ☐ False

   d. $14 + (-3) = 10 + 1$ ☐ True   ☐ False

---

5 A duck is sitting on a ledge that is 11 feet above the surface of a pond. The duck dives 27 feet straight down to get food at the bottom of the pond. Which expression represents the position of the bottom of the pond, in feet, relative to its surface level?

What does a negative value mean in this situation?

   A $27 + 11$ **C** $11 - (-27)$

   B $27 + (-11)$ **D** $11 + (-27)$

---

6 Which of the following are negative integers? Select all that are correct.

You may want to draw a number line and try sample numbers.

   A   the sum of two positive integers

   B   the sum of two negative integers

   C   the difference of a positive integer and an integer that is greater than it

   D   the difference of a negative integer and an integer that is greater than it but that is not its opposite

Dear Family,

Your child is learning about multiplying and dividing positive and negative integers.

Here are some examples of multiplying and dividing positive and negative integers that may be familiar to you.

- You set up an automatic deduction of a whole-dollar amount from a bank account each month to pay a bill. You can multiply the negative amount deducted by the number of months to find the amount deducted over a period of several months.

- You set up an automatic deposit of a whole-dollar amount to a savings account. You can multiply the positive amount deposited by the number of months to find the total amount deposited over a period of several months.

- A plane descends a number of feet in a number of seconds. You can divide the negative number of feet by the number of seconds to find the negative change in the plane's elevation per second.

Here are the rules for multiplying positive and negative integers.

positive $\times$ positive = positive
positive $\times$ negative = negative
negative $\times$ positive = negative
negative $\times$ negative = positive

Consider the following example:

A news account reported that the price of a stock dropped by 4 dollars a day for each of 3 consecutive days. How much did the stock price change over the 3 days?

On the next page you will see two different ways your child may use integer multiplication to find the amount that the price of the stock dropped.

A news account reported that the price of a stock dropped by
4 dollars a day for each of 3 consecutive days. How much did the
stock price change over the 3 days?

The change in the price of the stock can be represented by −4. To find
the total drop in the stock price you need to multiply −4 by 3.

One way:
Use repeated addition to represent multiplication.

The stock price dropped 4 dollars on each of 3 days.

$$3 \text{ groups of } -4 = (-4) + (-4) + (-4)$$
$$= -12$$

Another way:
Use a number line to represent multiplication.

Start at 0 and make 3 jumps of −4.

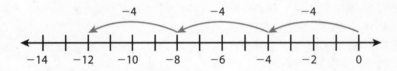

$$3 \cdot (-4) = -12$$

Answer: Both methods show that multiplying −4 by 3 gives a result of
−12. This means that the stock price changed by −12 dollars over the
3 days.

Multiply and Divide Positive and Negative Integers

Name: _____

Study the example showing how to add and subtract positive and negative integers. Then solve problems 1–6.

Example

Geneva and Juan are playing a game that involves a spinner. The table shows how the player's score changes according to the color the spinner lands on.

Color	Red	Yellow	Blue	Green
Number of Points	+2	−4	+3	−1

Juan has 32 points. Then his spin lands on yellow. What is his score now?

Yellow means Juan's score changes by −4 points.

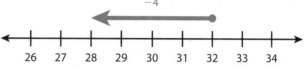

$32 - 4 = 32 + (-4) = 28$. Juan's score is 28 points.

---

1 Geneva has 24 points. Then her spin lands on blue. What is her score now? Explain.

_____

_____

2 Geneva and Juan start a new game. Each player has 0 points.

a. Geneva's first two spins are yellow and red. What is her score now? Explain.

_____

b. Juan's first two spins are red and green. What is his score now? Explain.

_____

c. Which player has a greater score now? Explain.

_____

Solve.

3 Describe a situation that the expression $-4 + (-1)$ could represent. Find the sum and tell what it represents in terms of the situation.

_____

_____

_____

4 A water bird is flying 11 feet above the surface of a pond. It dives 15 feet down and then rises 3 feet to catch a fish. What is the new position of the bird relative to the surface of the water?

Show your work.

Solution: _____

5 Steve's average long jump distance is 13 ft. He uses a table to keep track of the distance he jumps in six long jumps during his next practice.

Jump Number	1	2	3	4	5	6
Distance (ft)	14	11	15	12	13	10
Difference from Average of 13 (ft)	1	−2				

Complete the table. Then use the results to explain whether Steve's overall long jump performance on these six jumps is better or worse than average.

_____

_____

_____

6 Is the expression $|-3| + |4|$ equal to $|-3 + 4|$? Justify your answer.

_____

_____

Name: _____

Multiplying Integers

**Study the example problem showing how to multiply
positive and negative integers. Then solve problems 1–8.**

Example

Aidan likes to dive on vacation. He stops to take a picture
every 4 feet he dives. How has his elevation changed relative
to the surface of the water after he takes 5 pictures?

You can think of the change in Aidan's elevation between
pictures as −4. Aidan takes 5 pictures, so there are 5 groups
of −4.

Use the model to show the total change in Aidan's elevation
as jumps on a number line. Start at 0 and make jumps of −4.

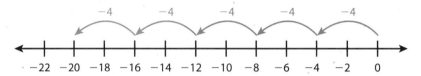

The number −20 represents the total change in Aidan's
elevation.

$$(-4) + (-4) + (-4) + (-4) + (-4) = -20$$

---

1 Rewrite the addition of groups as a multiplication
of groups.

$(-4) + (-4) + (-4) + (-4) + (-4) = $ _____

2 Complete: Adding 5 groups of (−4) is the same

as _____ 5 groups of (−4).

3 What is the total distance he dives in feet? _____

4 Use a model to multiply $5 \cdot (-3)$.

Show your work.

Solve.

5 A swimming pool has 500 gallons of water in it and is leaking. The change in the amount of water in the pool is −3 gallons per hour. How many gallons of water will the pool contain after 6 hours?

Show your work.

Solution: _____

6 Write the first two products in the table below. Then use the pattern in the products to write the last two products in the table.

	2 · (−2)	1 · (−2)	0 · (−2)	(−1) · (−2)	(−2) · (−2)
Product			0		

7 Complete each statement about multiplying positive and negative integers using the word *positive* or *negative*. For each statement, provide an example.

positive · positive = positive _____

positive · negative = _____

negative · negative = _____

8 Mrs. Krin has $300 deducted from her checking account every month for her car payment. She also has $150 deducted every month for her insurance. After 1 year, by how much do these payments change her checking account balance? Explain how you found your answer.

_____

_____

_____

_____

Name: _____

Dividing Integers

Study the example problem showing how to divide positive and negative integers. Then solve problems 1–7.

> **Example**
>
> Chen is labeling a thermometer that is used to measure very cold temperatures from 0°F to −40°F. He divides it into 8 equal sections. How many degrees does each section represent?
>
> Think: I need to divide −40 by 8, so I can ask $8 \cdot ? = -40$.
>
> $8 \cdot (-5) = -40$.
>
> This means that $-40 \div 8 = -5$.

1 Draw Chen's thermometer. Be sure to label each section.

2 Chen labels another thermometer that uses 10 different sections. Complete the table for this thermometer.

Total number of degrees (°F)	÷	Number of sections	=	Degrees in each section (°F)
−40			=	

3 A scuba diver descends 48 feet in 4 minutes. What is the diver's average change in position per minute relative to where she started?

_____

Lesson 4 Multiply and Divide Positive and Negative Integers

Solve.

4 Multiplication and division are related operations. Look at these examples.

$2 \cdot 4 = 8$	$(-2) \cdot (-4) = 8$	$-2 \cdot 4 = -8$	$2 \cdot (-4) = -8$
$8 \div 4 = 2$	$8 \div (-4) = -2$	$-8 \div 4 = -2$	$-8 \div (-4) = 2$

Think about the signs of the factors and the sign of the product in the multiplication problems. How do the signs of the numbers you are dividing relate to their quotients?

_____

_____

_____

5 Describe a situation that the expression $-15 \div (-5)$ could represent. Find the quotient and tell what it represents in terms of the situation.

_____

_____

_____

6 The low temperatures in degrees Fahrenheit in Marsh City during a week in January were:

$-3, -5, 3, 7, -2, -2, -5$

What was the average low temperature for that week?

Show your work.

Solution: _____

7 The quotient $x \div 5$ is a negative integer. Name two integers that x could represent and find the quotients.

_____

Name: _____

Multiply and Divide Positive and Negative Integers

Solve the problems.

1 A whale dives at a speed of 3 feet per second. What is the change in the position of the whale relative to where it started after 12 seconds?

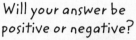

Will your answer be positive or negative?

A   −36 feet   **C**   4 feet

B   −4 feet   **D**   36 feet

2 Tell whether each equation is *True* or *False*.

a. $-7 \cdot 8 = 7 \cdot (-8)$ ☐ True   ☐ False

b. $-7 \cdot (-8) = 7 \cdot 8$ ☐ True   ☐ False

c. $7 \cdot (-8) = 7 \cdot 8$ ☐ True   ☐ False

How can the signs of the factors in each multiplication equation help you solve this problem?

3 Myra withdraws the same amount of money from her checking account each week. In 4 weeks, she withdraws a total of $200. Which equation represents the amount of money her account changes by each week?

What can the signs of the numbers in a division problem tell you about the quotient?

A $-200 \div (-4) = 50$

B $-200 \div 4 = -50$

C $-200 \div 4 = 50$

D $-200 \div (-4) = -50$

Sam chose **C** as the correct answer. How did he get that answer?

_____

_____

Solve.

4 Kain made two number cubes to use in a game. The faces on each cube contain the numbers 1, −2, 3, −4, 5, and −6. After Kain rolls the two cubes, he multiplies the two numbers.

What is true about the signs of two factors if their product is positive?

a. Give an example of two numbers that Kain could roll to get a positive product.

_____

_____

b. Give an example of two numbers that Kain could roll to get a negative product.

_____

_____

5 Savannah solves each of the following problems as shown below.

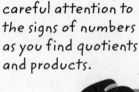

Remember to pay careful attention to the signs of numbers as you find quotients and products.

a. $-6 \cdot 12 \div (-4) = 18$

b. $8 \cdot (-3) \div 6 = -4$

c. $-40 \cdot (-2) \div (-10) = 8$

d. $-7 \cdot 5 \cdot (-2) \div 5 = 14$

Are the answers correct? Explain any incorrect answers.

_____

_____

_____

_____

_____

Dear Family,

> **Your child is learning about terminating and repeating decimals.**

A fraction can be written as a decimal. Sometimes decimals are more convenient to work with than fractions. Because a fraction represents division, you can divide to write a fraction as a decimal. Here are some examples:

$\frac{5}{8}$ means $5 \div 8$.

$$
\begin{array}{r}
0.625 \\
8\overline{)5.000} \\
-48 \\
\hline
20 \\
-16 \\
\hline
40 \\
-40 \\
\hline
0
\end{array}
$$

$\frac{2}{3}$ means $2 \div 3$.

$$
\begin{array}{r}
0.666\ldots \\
3\overline{)2.000} \\
-18 \\
\hline
20 \\
-18 \\
\hline
20 \\
-18 \\
\hline
2
\end{array}
$$

The decimal 0.625 is a *terminating decimal*. A terminating decimal terminates, or ends. The decimal 0.666… is a *repeating decimal*. The digit 6 repeats without end.

Consider this situation:

Tyrone and Henry are practicing soccer. Tyrone kicks the ball into the net 4 out of 15 times. Henry kicks the ball into the net 9 out of 20 times. Write decimals to represent how often Tyrone and Henry each kick the ball into the net.

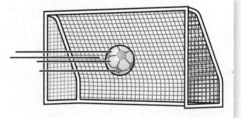

The next page shows how your child can write decimals that show how often each boy kicks the soccer ball into the net.

Tyrone kicks a soccer ball into the net 4 out of 15 times. Henry kicks a soccer ball into the net 9 out of 20 times. Write decimals to represent how often Tyrone and Henry each kick the ball into the net.

You can write 4 out of 15 times as the fraction $\frac{4}{15}$ and 9 out of 20 times as the fraction $\frac{9}{20}$.

You can start by estimating so that you know about what the decimal should be.

Tyrone:

$\frac{4}{15}$ is between $\frac{3}{15}$ and $\frac{5}{15}$.

$\frac{3}{15} = \frac{1}{5}$ and $\frac{5}{15} = \frac{1}{3}$

So, $\frac{4}{15}$ is between 0.2 and $0.\overline{3}$.

Henry:

$\frac{9}{20}$ is between $\frac{8}{20}$ and $\frac{10}{20}$.

$\frac{8}{20} = \frac{2}{5}$ and $\frac{10}{20} = \frac{1}{2}$

So, $\frac{9}{20}$ is between 0.4 and 0.5.

Now you can use division to find the decimals for $\frac{4}{15}$ and $\frac{9}{20}$.

$$
\begin{array}{r}
0.266... \\
15\overline{)4.000} \\
-30 \\
\hline
100 \\
-90 \\
\hline
100 \\
-90 \\
\hline
10
\end{array}
$$

$$
\begin{array}{r}
0.45 \\
20\overline{)9.00} \\
-80 \\
\hline
100 \\
-100 \\
\hline
0
\end{array}
$$

The fraction $\frac{4}{15}$ is equivalent to the repeating decimal $0.2\overline{6}$.

The fraction $\frac{9}{20}$ is equivalent to the terminating decimal 0.45.

Answer: The decimal $0.2\overline{6}$ represents how often Tyrone kicks the soccer ball into the net, and the decimal 0.45 represents how often Henry kicks the soccer ball into the net.

Terminating and Repeating Decimals

Name: _____

Study the example showing fractions as division. Then solve problems 1–5.

Example

A teacher has 3 cups of brown rice to share equally among 4 students in cooking class. How much rice will each student get?

You can model this problem with a picture.

Look at one of the cups. One cup divided among 4 students is $\frac{1}{4}$ cup.

You can think of this as $1 \div 4 = \frac{1}{4}$.

$\frac{1}{4}$ cup $\frac{1}{4}$ cup $\frac{1}{4}$ cup

The teacher has 3 cups, so each student will receive $\frac{3}{4}$ cup of rice.

You can think of this as $\frac{1}{4} \times 3 = \frac{3}{4}$ or $3 \div 4 = \frac{3}{4}$.

---

1 The teacher has 5 cups of broth to share among the 4 students.

   a. How much broth will each student get? Draw a model to explain your answer.

     _____

   b. Will each student get more than or less than 1 cup of broth? Explain.

     _____

2 What if the teacher divides the 5 cups of broth among 6 students? Will each student get more than or less than 1 cup of broth? Explain.

_____

Solve.

3 Five seventh-grade students are decorating 3 bulletin boards and want to divide the work equally.

a. Will each student decorate more than or less than 1 bulletin board? Explain how you know.

_____

_____

b. How many fifths of a bulletin board are there in 3 bulletin boards? Use a model to explain.

_____

c. How many fifths of a bulletin board will each student decorate?

_____ fifths

d. Write this as a fraction of a bulletin board.

_____ of a bulletin board

4 A science teacher has 15 ounces of vinegar to divide equally among 8 students for an experiment. Matt said that each student should get $\frac{8}{15}$ ounce. How did he get that answer? Do you agree? Explain.

_____

_____

5 One restaurant uses 5 quarts of soup to make 20 equal servings. Another restaurant uses 7 quarts of soup to make 25 equal servings. Which restaurant has larger servings of soup? Write division expressions to represent the problem and then solve.

Show your work.

Solution: _____

Name: _____

Study the example showing how to use patterns to write fractions as equivalent decimals. Then solve problems 1–7.

Example

Carlos knows that $\frac{1}{20} = 0.05$. He can use a table of values to find a pattern that will help him find the decimal forms of $\frac{2}{20}$, $\frac{3}{20}$, $\frac{4}{20}$, and $\frac{5}{20}$.

$$\begin{array}{r} 0.05 \\ 20\overline{)1.00} \\ -1\,00 \\ \hline 0 \end{array}$$

Fraction	Decimal
$\frac{1}{20}$	0.05
$\frac{2}{20}$	0.10
$\frac{3}{20}$	0.15
$\frac{4}{20}$	0.20
$\frac{5}{20}$	0.25

Because $\frac{2}{20}$ is twice $\frac{1}{20}$, the decimal form of $\frac{2}{20}$ is twice 0.05, or 0.10.

1 Describe the patterns in the table.

   a. What is the pattern in the first column?

   _____

   b. What is the pattern in the second column?

   _____

   c. How can you use the fraction in the first column to write the equivalent decimal in the second column?

   _____

   _____

2 Explain how you can use the patterns in the table to find the decimal form of $\frac{17}{20}$.

   _____

   _____

Lesson 5 Terminating and Repeating Decimals   **41**

Solve.

3 What kind of decimal is 0.05? How do you know?

_____

4 Use the fact that $\frac{1}{20} = 0.05$ to write the decimal form of the unit fractions $\frac{1}{10}, \frac{1}{5}$, and $\frac{1}{4}$ in the table below.

Unit Fraction	Decimal
$\frac{1}{10}$	
$\frac{1}{5}$	
$\frac{1}{4}$	

5 Explain how you can find each decimal form in problem 4 using the decimal form of $\frac{1}{20}$.

_____

_____

_____

6 Marita knows that $\frac{1}{5}$ written as a decimal is 0.20.

  a. How can she find the decimal form of $\frac{9}{5}$ without dividing?

  _____

  b. What is another way that Marita could figure out the decimal form of $\frac{9}{5}$ without dividing?

  _____

  _____

7 Chuck knows that $\frac{1}{50} = 0.02$. How can he use this information to find the fraction form for the decimal 0.86?

_____

_____

_____

Vocabulary

terminating decimal
a decimal that ends, or terminates.
0.5; 4.08; 0.300

Name: _____

Writing Fractions as Decimals

Study the example problem showing how to write a fraction as a decimal. Then solve problems 1–7.

Example

A relay race is 2 miles long. Eleven students will run the relay, splitting the distance as equally as possible for a distance of about $\frac{2}{11}$ mile each. Does the first relay exchange occur before or after 0.2 mile?

$$\frac{2}{11} = 2 \div 11$$

$$
\begin{array}{r}
0.1818\ldots \\
11\overline{)2.0000} \\
-11 \\
\hline
90 \\
-88 \\
\hline
20 \\
-11 \\
\hline
90 \\
-88 \\
\hline
2
\end{array}
$$

$$\frac{2}{11} = 0.1818\ldots = 0.\overline{18}$$

The first relay exchange occurs *before* 0.2 mile because $0.\overline{18} < 0.2$.

1 How do you know that the decimal for $\frac{2}{11}$ repeats without end?

_____

_____

2 Between which two tenths of a mile will the second relay exchange occur? Explain.

_____

_____

_____

_____

3 Will there be more than one relay exchange between 2 consecutive tenths of a mile? Explain.

_____

_____

Vocabulary

repeating decimal a decimal that never ends but instead repeats the same digit or digits over and over. $0.6666\ldots = 0.\overline{6}$

Solve.

4 You saw on the previous page that $\frac{2}{11} = 0.\overline{18}$. Show how you can use what you know about the decimal for $\frac{2}{11}$ to find the decimal for $\frac{1}{11}$.

_____

5 A 9-member team plans to run a 4-mile relay race. Distance markers are placed on the racecourse every 0.25 mile.

   a. Place an X on the number line at the approximate locations where the relay exchanges will take place.

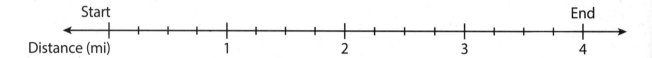

   b. Will any of the relay exchanges take place at any of the 0.25-mile markers? If so, which one(s)? List the locations of all of the exchanges in decimal form.

   _____

6 If the decimal form for a unit fraction is a repeating decimal, is it possible for a multiple of that fraction to have a decimal form that is not a repeating decimal? Use examples to explain your reasoning.

_____

_____

7 Mario claims that if the denominator of a fraction is a prime number, then its decimal form is a repeating decimal. Do you agree? Use an example to explain.

_____

_____

Name: _____

Terminating and Repeating Decimals

Solve the problems.

---

1 Carla says that $\frac{5}{6}$ is greater than 0.8. Is she correct?

Show your work.

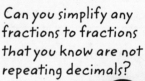

How can you write a fraction as a division problem?

Solution: _____

---

2 Which of the following are repeating decimals when written in decimal form? Select all that apply.

A $\frac{11}{16}$

B $\frac{8}{11}$

C $\frac{3}{9}$

D $\frac{9}{18}$

Can you simplify any fractions to fractions that you know are not repeating decimals?

---

3 Complete the table. Then describe a pattern in the decimal forms of the fractions.

Unit Fraction	$\frac{1}{2}$	$\frac{1}{3}$	$\frac{1}{4}$	$\frac{1}{5}$	$\frac{1}{6}$
Decimal	0.5				

What happens to the value of the decimal as the denominator of the fraction increases?

_____

_____

_____

Solve.

4 Mark estimates that he spends $\frac{3}{8}$ of his money on lunches. What percent of his money does he spend on lunches?

A 2.6%   **C** 26%

B 3.75%   **D** 37.5%

Sue chose **B** as the correct answer. How did she get that answer?

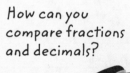

When you write a decimal as a percent, what do you need to do to the decimal point?

_____

_____

5 Mrs. Gelb is making costumes for a play. The table shows how many yards of each color ribbon are needed and how many yards she has on hand.

How can you compare fractions and decimals?

Color	Yards She Needs	Yards She Has
Red	$2\frac{5}{8}$	2.5
Green	$\frac{7}{8}$	0.36
Black	$4\frac{3}{8}$	4.5

Tell whether each statement is *True* or *False*.

a. She does not need to buy any black ribbon.   ☐ True ☐ False

b. She needs to buy $\frac{3}{8}$ yard of red ribbon.   ☐ True ☐ False

c. She needs to buy at least $\frac{3}{5}$ yard of green ribbon.   ☐ True ☐ False

6 Write a fraction and its decimal equivalent for the following conditions.

What fractions can you think of that you know repeat? When will a fraction be greater than 1?

a. a fraction that is a repeating decimal between 0.25 and 0.5

_____

b. a fraction that is a repeating decimal between 0.5 and 1

_____

c. a fraction that is a terminating decimal between 1.25 and 1.5

_____

Dear Family,

Your child is learning about multiplying and dividing rational numbers.

Your child has already learned to multiply and divide whole numbers, fractions, decimals, and integers. Now your child will multiply and divide rational numbers, including fractions and decimals that have positive and negative values.

When you multiply positive and negative fractions and decimals, you use the same rules as when you multiply positive and negative integers.

The table on the right shows the rules for how the signs of the factors affect the sign of the product when you multiply positive and negative numbers, and gives examples.

Rule	Example
positive × positive = positive	$\frac{3}{4} \times \frac{1}{2} = \frac{3}{8}$
positive × negative = negative	$4.2 \times (-1.5) = -6.3$
negative × positive = negative	$-\frac{1}{5} \times \frac{4}{3} = -\frac{4}{15}$
negative × negative = positive	$-3.7 \times -2.6 = 9.62$

Because any division problem can also be written as a multiplication problem, you can use the same rules when you divide.

Consider the following example:

Brian, Stacy, and Eleni are climbing down a rock-climbing wall. Brian changes his position by $-\frac{14}{6}$ meters from the top of the climbing wall. Stacy's change in position is half of Brian's. Eleni's change in position is 3 times Brian's. By how much did Stacy's and Eleni's positions change relative to the top of the climbing wall?

On the next page you will see two different ways in which your child might multiply numbers to find Stacy's and Eleni's changes in position.

Brian changes his position by $-\frac{14}{6}$ meters from the top of the climbing wall. Stacy's change in position is half of Brian's. Eleni's change in position is 3 times Brian's. By how much did Stacy's and Eleni's positions change relative to the top of the climbing wall?

One way:
Use number lines to model the problem.

Let 0 represent the top of the rock climbing wall. Divide each whole unit into sixths.

Brian's change in position is $-\frac{14}{6}$. Stacy's change in position is $\frac{1}{2}$ of $-\frac{14}{6}$, or $-\frac{7}{6}$. Eleni's change in position is 3 times $-\frac{14}{6}$, or $-\frac{42}{6}$, which is the same as -7.

Another way:
Use multiplication to find each person's change in position.

Brian: $-\frac{14}{6}$ meters

Stacy: $\frac{1}{2} \times \left(-\frac{14}{6}\right) = -\frac{14}{12}$

$= -\frac{7}{6}$ or $-1\frac{1}{6}$

Eleni: $3 \times \left(-\frac{14}{6}\right) = -\frac{42}{6}$

$= -7$

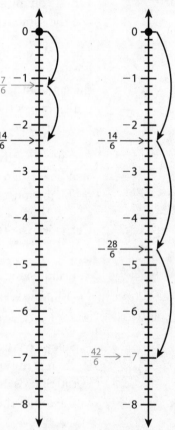

Answer: Both methods show that $\frac{1}{2} \times \left(-\frac{14}{6}\right) = -\frac{7}{6}$, or $-1\frac{1}{6}$, and that $3 \times \left(-\frac{14}{6}\right) = -\frac{42}{6}$, or -7, meaning that Stacy's position changed by $-1\frac{1}{6}$ meters and Eleni's position changed by -7 meters.

Multiply and Divide Rational Numbers

Name: _____

Study the example problem showing how to use repeated addition to multiply a positive and a negative integer. Then solve problems 1–6.

Example

Dues for the art club are $2 per week. Noriko pays $2 each week from her bank account for her art club dues. At the end of 5 weeks, what is the change in the amount of money in Noriko's account?

You can think of this as 5 groups of (−2).

5 groups of $(−2) = (−2) + (−2) + (−2) + (−2) + (−2)$.

You can start at 0 and make 5 jumps of −2.

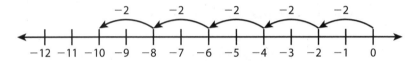

$(−2) + (−2) + (−2) + (−2) + (−2) = −10$

So, Noriko's account changes by −$10.

---

1 Complete the table and describe the pattern in the products.

_____

2 Rewrite the repeated addition expression as a multiplication expression and find the product.

a. $(−2) + (−2) + (−2) + (−2) + (−2) =$ _____ $• (−2) =$ _____

b. $(−3) + (−3) + (−3) + (−3) + (−3) + (−3) =$ _____

c. $(−5) + (−5) + (−5) =$ _____

Multiplication	Product
$−2 • 3$	$−6$
$−2 • 2$	$−4$
$−2 • 1$	$−2$
$−2 • 0$	
$−2 • (−1)$	
$−2 • (−2)$	
$−2 • (−3)$	

+2

+2

Solve.

3 Write and simplify a multiplication expression for each problem. Explain what the product means.

a. The temperature dropped 8 degrees every hour. What was the change in temperature after 4 hours?

_____

b. Mae loses 3 points for each wrong answer on a test. How does her score change if she has 7 wrong answers?

_____

4 Carlo is playing a game with the cards shown. He draws cards at random and multiplies the numbers.

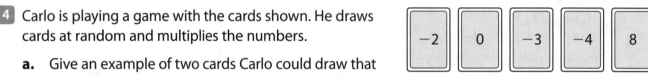

a. Give an example of two cards Carlo could draw that have a positive product. Find the product.

_____

b. Give an example of two cards Carlo could draw that have a negative product. Find the product.

_____

5 Each month Marla pays a $30 cell phone bill from her back account. At the end of one year, what is the change in the amount of money in Marla's account because of her cell phone bill? Write a multiplication equation to represent the problem. Explain what the product represents.

_____

6 How many integers must be negative for the product of three integers to be negative? Explain. Find two different groups of three integers whose product is −12.

Show your work.

Solution: _____

_____

_____

Name: _____

Multiply Rational Numbers

Study the example problem showing how to multiply rational numbers. Then solve problems 1–8.

Example

The temperature of a liquid in an experiment is 0°C at 9 AM.

The experiment calls for the temperature to change $-\frac{5}{4}$°C

every hour. What will the temperature be at noon?

The model shows that the temperature will be $-\frac{15}{4}$°C, or

$-3\frac{3}{4}$°C, at noon.

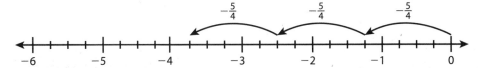

You can also use multiplication to solve:

$$3 \cdot \left(-\frac{5}{4}\right) = -\frac{15}{4} = -3\frac{3}{4}$$

---

1 If the liquid continues to cool at the same rate, what will the temperature be at 3 PM? Explain.

_____

_____

2 If the experiment called for the temperature of the liquid

to change by $-\frac{3}{4}$°C each hour, what would the

temperature be at noon? Explain.

_____

3 In a different experiment, a liquid must be cooled 6 times as fast as the liquid in the example, but it must still start at 0°C.

a. What will the change in temperature be each hour? Write and evaluate an expression to explain.

_____

b. What will the temperature be after 4 hours? Write and evaluate an expression to explain.

_____

　　Lesson 6 Multiply and Divide Rational Numbers　**51**

Solve.

4 Evaluate the products.

  a. $4 \times \left(-\dfrac{3}{8}\right) =$ _____   **b.** $(-4) \times \left(-\dfrac{3}{8}\right) =$ _____

5 How can you use the rules for multiplying positive and negative numbers to check that your answers to problem 4 have the correct sign?

_____

_____

6 A deep sea diver changes his position relative to the surface of the water by $-\dfrac{7}{2}$ meters per minute. Write and evaluate an expression to show his position after 3 minutes if he starts at the surface of the water.

_____

7 Evaluate the products. Write your answers in simplest form.

  a. $-\dfrac{4}{5} \times \left(-\dfrac{5}{8}\right) =$ _____   **b.** $\left(-\dfrac{3}{10}\right) \times \left(\dfrac{2}{7}\right) =$ _____

8 The height of a 9-inch candle changes at a rate of $-\dfrac{2}{3}$ inch per hour when it is burning. How long will it take the candle to burn completely?

Show your work.

Solution: _____

Name: _____

Divide Rational Numbers

Study the example problem showing how to divide rational numbers. Then solve problems 1–6.

Example

The position of a submersible water vehicle, relative to sea level, changes by −0.5 mile each hour. After how many hours will the vehicle's position have changed by −2.5 miles?

You can use a table to understand the problem.

You can also use division to understand the problem.

$(-2.5) \div (-0.5) = -25 \div (-5) = 5$

Time (h)	Position
0	0
1	−0.5
2	−1.0
3	−1.5
4	−2.0
5	−2.5

−0.5
−0.5
−0.5
−0.5
−0.5

1 You can also use repeated addition to evaluate the quotient $(-2.5) \div (-0.5)$. Complete.

$-2.5 = (-0.5) + $ _____

There are _____ groups of −0.5 in _____.

It will take _____ hours for the submersible's position to change by −2.5 miles.

2 Mariella's bank statement shows a change of −$2.50 in her account each week.

a. Complete the table to see how many weeks it will be before the change in Mariella's account is −$20.

Number of Weeks	1	2	3	4	5	6	7	8
Change in Account ($)	−2.5	−5.0	−7.5					

b. Why are the amounts in the table negative?

_____

c. How many weeks will it take for the the amount deducted to total −$20? _____

Solve.

3 A pitcher contains 28 fluid ounces of juice. How many 4-ounce servings can you pour before the pitcher is empty? Complete the repeated subtraction to solve.

$-28 = (-4) + $ _____

I can pour _____ four-ounce glasses of juice.

4 A small inflatable pool holds 10 gallons of water. A tiny leak causes the amount of water in the pool to change by -0.05 gallon each hour until the pool is empty.

a. Write the numbers that represent each quantity.

change in amount of water per hour = _____

total change in amount of water = _____

b. Will you multiply or divide to find how many hours it will take for the pool to be empty? Will the answer be positive or negative?

_____

_____

c. How many hours will it take for the pool to be

empty? _____ hours

5 The temperature at 6 PM was 0°F. At 10 PM the temperature was -11.2°F. Write an expression that you can use to find the average change in temperature per hour during that time. Then evaluate the expression.

_____

6 Marlene is solving a number puzzle involving three rational numbers a, b, and c. Here are her clues:

• The quotient of a and c is 8.

• The product of a and c is 2.

• The quotient of a and b is -16.

• The product of a and b is -1.

• The quotient of b and c is -0.5.

What are the three numbers in Marlene's puzzle?

_____

Lesson 6 Multiply and Divide Rational Numbers

Name: _____

Multiply and Divide Rational Numbers

Solve the problems.

1 Imamu pays $30 each month for his gym membership. What is the change in the amount of money in his account after $\frac{2}{3}$ of a year?

How many months are in a year?

A	−$120	**C**	−$270
B	−$240	**D**	−$360

Bob chose **A** as the correct answer. How did he get that answer?

_____

_____

2 Trevon, Leah, and Beth are playing a computer game. Trevon scored −8. Beth's score was $\frac{3}{4}$ of Trevon's score, and Leah's score was $\frac{1}{4}$ of Beth's score. What was Leah's score?

Will Leah's score be positive or negative?

A	$-\frac{2}{3}$	**C**	$\frac{2}{3}$
B	$-\frac{3}{2}$	**D**	$\frac{3}{2}$

3 Paula cut ribbon from a spool for a craft project. Each piece of ribbon changed the length of the ribbon remaining on the spool by −1.2 feet. When Paula finished, the length of ribbon on the spool had changed by $-9\frac{3}{5}$ feet. How many pieces of ribbon did Paula cut?

Can writing both numbers as either fractions or decimals help you?

Show your work.

Solution: _____

Solve.

---

4 Craig is making 3 recipes for his party. He has a container of flour on his kitchen scale. The table shows the total change in weight of the flour on the scale after each of the 3 recipes. What is the average change in the amount of flour, in ounces, used in the 3 recipes?

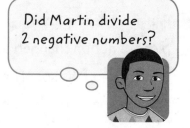

How can you find an average?

Flour Used	After Recipe 1	After Recipe 2	After Recipe 3
Change in Weight (oz)	-2	$-3\frac{1}{2}$	$-4\frac{1}{2}$

A $-\frac{3}{2}$

C $-3\frac{1}{3}$

B $-2\frac{1}{2}$

D $-7\frac{1}{2}$

---

5 On the number line, a and b are rational numbers. Tell whether each statement is *True* or *False*.

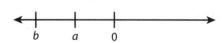

How can you tell whether a product or quotient is positive or negative?

a. $a \cdot b$ is negative. ☐ True ☐ False

b. $a \div b$ is greater than 0. ☐ True ☐ False

c. $b \div a$ is greater than $a \div b$. ☐ True ☐ False

d. $a \cdot b = b \cdot a$ ☐ True ☐ False

---

6 Martin chose two of the cards below. When he found the quotient of the numbers, his answer was $-\frac{16}{9}$. Write the division problem that Martin solved.

Did Martin divide 2 negative numbers?

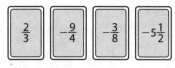

Show your work.

Solution: _____

Dear Family,

> **Your child is learning about adding and subtracting rational numbers.**

Your child has already learned to add and subtract integers. Now your child will add and subtract rational numbers.

You add and subtract positive and negative fractions and decimals in the same way that you add and subtract positive and negative integers. Here are two examples.

Addition

$$-0.2 + 0.6$$

$$-0.2 + 0.6 = 0.4$$

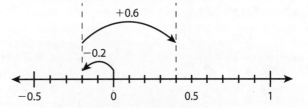

Subtraction

$$\frac{2}{6} - \frac{7}{6}$$

Rewrite the problem as addition using the additive inverse.

$$\frac{2}{6} + \left(-\frac{7}{6}\right) = -\frac{5}{6}$$

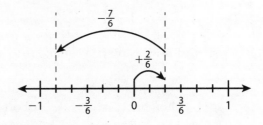

Consider this situation:

A scientist records erosion of $\frac{1}{2}$ foot on a beach shoreline after a storm. Previous storms had already eroded the shoreline by $\frac{5}{6}$ foot. What is the total change to the beach shoreline due to storm erosion?

The next page shows two different ways your child might add negative fractions in order to find the total change to the beach shoreline.

Lesson 7 Add and Subtract Rational Numbers

NEXT

A scientist records $\frac{1}{2}$ foot of erosion on a beach shoreline after a storm. Previous storms had eroded the shoreline by $\frac{5}{6}$ foot. What is the total change to the beach shoreline due to storm erosion?

To find the change to the beach shoreline, you add $-\frac{1}{2}$ and $-\frac{5}{6}$.

One way: Use a number line to add negative fractions.

$$-\frac{1}{2} + \left(-\frac{5}{6}\right)$$

Use a common denominator of 6.

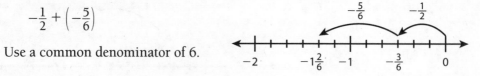

Write $-\frac{1}{2}$ as the equivalent fraction $-\frac{3}{6}$.

$$-\frac{3}{6} + \left(-\frac{5}{6}\right) = -\frac{8}{6}$$

Another way: Use equations to add negative fractions.

Overall change to shoreline after a storm	+	Change to shoreline from previous storms	=	Overall change to shoreline after all the storms
$\left(-\frac{1}{2}\right)$	+	$\left(-\frac{5}{6}\right)$	=	?

Solve the equation: $-\frac{1}{2} + \left(-\frac{5}{6}\right) = -\frac{3}{6} + \left(-\frac{5}{6}\right)$

$$= -\frac{8}{6}$$

Answer: Both methods show that $-\frac{1}{2} + \left(-\frac{5}{6}\right) = -\frac{8}{6}$, so the total change to the beach shoreline due to storm erosion is $-\frac{8}{6}$ feet. Since you can write $-\frac{8}{6}$ as $-\frac{4}{3}$ or $-1\frac{1}{3}$, these are also correct answers.

Add and Subtract Rational Numbers

Name: _____

Study the example showing how to add positive and negative integers. Then solve problems 1–5.

Example

Guy, Ian, and Bella play a game in which they spin a spinner with both positive and negative numbers on it. They add the values of each spin. The player with the lowest total score wins.

	Guy	Ian	Bella
Score, Spin 1	4	−6	−2
Score, Spin 2	−3	−2	4
Total Score	4 + (−3)	−6 + (−2)	−2 + 4

You can add the numbers on a number line to find each person's total score.

For example, you can find Guy's total score by locating 4 on the number line and moving left 3 units. His final score is 1.

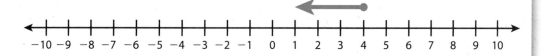

1 Use this number line to find Ian's final score.

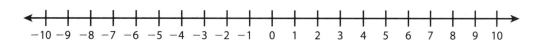

final score: _____

2 Use this number line to find Bella's final score.

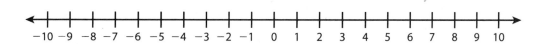

final score: _____

Lesson 7 Add and Subtract Rational Numbers

Solve.

3 You can write a subtraction problem as an addition problem by adding the opposite of the number. For example, $1 - 5 = 1 + (-5)$. Write each of the following subtraction problems as addition problems. Then simplify to find the difference.

a. $5 - 8$

_____

_____

b. $-9 - (-7)$

_____

_____

c. $-3 - 8$

_____

_____

d. $-1 - (-4)$

_____

_____

4 Jane and Sheryl are scuba diving. Relative to the surface of the water, Jane's position is -14 feet and Sheryl's position is -10 feet. Write and evaluate a subtraction expression that shows Jane's position relative to Sheryl's position.

_____

5 Both expressions $-3 - (-7)$ and $-7 - (-3)$ involve the difference of two negative numbers.

a. Explain when the difference of two negative numbers is negative and when it is positive.

_____

_____

_____

_____

b. Write another subtraction problem involving two negative numbers that has a positive difference. Then write another subtraction problem involving two negative numbers that has a negative difference.

_____

Name: _____

Add Negative Fractions

Study the example problem showing how to add negative fractions. Then solve problems 1–6.

Example

Willie is making cookies. From a bag of sugar, he removed $1\frac{1}{4}$ cups for the cookie dough and $\frac{3}{8}$ cup to sprinkle on top. What number represents the total change in the amount of sugar in the bag?

You can use a number line to solve this problem.

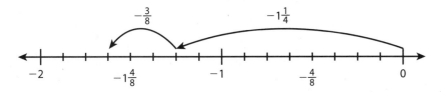

The model shows that the total change in the amount of sugar in the bag is $-1\frac{5}{8}$ cups.

You can also use an equation to find the solution.

Change in sugar for dough	+	Change in sugar for sprinkles	=	Overall change
$-1\frac{1}{4}$	+	$\left(-\frac{3}{8}\right)$	=	$-1\frac{5}{8}$

1 Use a common denominator to find $-1\frac{1}{4} + \left(-\frac{3}{8}\right)$.

_____

2 Use a common denominator to find $-\frac{2}{3} + \left(-\frac{4}{5}\right)$.

Show your work.

Solution: _____

Solve.

3 Serena is building a bookcase. She cuts two pieces of wood from one board. One piece is $1\frac{7}{8}$ feet long and another is $3\frac{1}{2}$ feet long. What is the total change in the length of the original board?

Show your work.

Solution: _____

4 In an experiment, the temperature of a solution is $-\frac{7}{8}$°F. The temperature drops $1\frac{1}{2}$ °F. What is the temperature after the drop?

Show your work.

Solution: _____

5 The sum of two negative fractions with different denominators is $-\frac{7}{10}$. What are two possible fractions?

Show your work.

Solution: _____

6 Find the sum.

a. $-2\frac{1}{10} + \left(-4\frac{4}{5}\right)$ _____

b. $-3\frac{5}{6} + \left(-1\frac{7}{12}\right)$ _____

Name: _____

Add and Subtract Rational Numbers

Study the example problem showing how to add and subtract rational numbers. Then solve problems 1–7.

Example

On a test, wrong answers are worth −5.25 points and right answers are worth 3.5 points. So far, Marshall has one right answer and one wrong answer. What is Marshall's current score?

You can solve this problem using a number line.

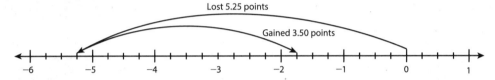

Lost 5.25 points

Gained 3.50 points

The number line model shows that Marshall's current score is −1.75.

---

1 Write an addition equation to represent the situation.

_____

2 Find $-5\frac{1}{4} + 3\frac{1}{2}$. Explain how you found your answer.

_____

_____

3 Elaine says that when you add two rational numbers, the sign depends on how many negative numbers you have. Do you agree with Elaine? Explain your answer.

_____

_____

_____

_____

Lesson 7 Add and Subtract Rational Numbers   **63**

Solve.

4 A gardener cuts a plant down by $1\frac{5}{8}$ inches. The plant then grows $9\frac{1}{4}$ more inches. What is the total change in the height of the plant? Explain.

Show your work.

Solution: _____

5 Solve each problem.

   a. What is $-4.3 - (-6.8)$? _____

   b. What is $1\frac{3}{5} + \left(-2\frac{7}{10}\right)$? _____

6 You are playing a game. You lose 4.8 points, lose another 7.6 points, and then win 2.5 points. What is the overall change in your score?

Show your work.

Solution: _____

7 Find the number that makes the equation true.

$$-\frac{7}{10} + ? = -2\frac{9}{20}$$

Show your work.

Solution: _____

Name: _____

Add and Subtract Rational Numbers

Solve the problems.

1 What is $-8.3 - (-5.4)$?

A -13.7 **C** 2.9

B -2.9 **D** 13.7

Lon chose A as the correct answer. How did he get that answer?

_____

_____

How do you subtract a negative number?

2 Michelle poured $\frac{7}{8}$ cup of water from a pitcher into a glass. Then she poured another $\frac{2}{3}$ cup. What is the change in the amount of water in the pitcher? Explain.

_____

_____

Can a common denominator help you?

3 Which expressions are equal to $0.50 - (-1.75)$? Select all that apply.

A $\frac{1}{50} - \left(-1\frac{3}{4}\right)$ **C** $0.50 + 1.75$

B $-0.50 - 1.75$ **D** $\frac{1}{2} + 1\frac{3}{4}$

How do you write a decimal as a fraction?

4 Tell whether each statement is *True* or *False*.

a. $0.45 - (-0.4) = 0.85$ ☐ True   ☐ False

b. $-1\frac{5}{8} - \left(-5\frac{5}{8}\right) = -7\frac{1}{4}$ ☐ True   ☐ False

c. $-7\frac{3}{7} + \frac{1}{7} = -7\frac{2}{7}$ ☐ True   ☐ False

What is the first step in solving these problems?

Solve.

5 Consider the following equation.

$$-\frac{5}{6} + \square = \text{a negative number}$$

Will a number that makes the equation true be positive or negative?

a. Write a fraction that makes this equation true.

_____

b. Show that your fraction makes the equation true.

_____

_____

6 During a hot summer week, the water level in Wei's pool decreased by 1.9 centimeters. Wei added water to the pool, increasing the level by 3.5 centimeters. During the next week, the water level decreased by 2.4 centimeters. How does the new water level compare to the original water level?

What do positive and negative values represent in this situation?

Show your work.

Solution: _____

_____

7 If a is a negative rational number and b is a positive rational number, which of the following must be true? Give an example for the statements that are true and a counterexample for the statements that are false.

a. $a - b$ is positive.

_____

b. $b - a$ is positive.

_____

c. $b + (-a)$ is negative.

_____

Dear Family,

Your child is learning about solving problems with rational numbers.

Real-life situations often involve fractional quantities and decimal amounts. Here are some examples.

- You want to build a fence that is 60 feet long. How many $7\frac{1}{2}$ - foot long fence sections will you need?

- You are painting 3 rooms in your house and want to know how many gallons of paint to buy if each room requires $1\frac{3}{4}$ gallons of paint.

- You are purchasing items that cost $32.29, $24.19, and $21.89 with a gift card that has $83.62 remaining on it. Is the cost of the three items, plus tax, more or less than the amount on the gift card?

You can estimate to find an approximate solution in each situation. But to find the actual solution you need to calculate with fractions and decimals.

Consider the following example:

Ms. Scanlon has an automatic deposit of $41.60 into her bank account on Wednesday. On Thursday, she uses online banking to pay two bills for $17.15 and $26.85 from the account. Does Ms. Scanlon have more or less money in the account after the withdrawals than she did before the deposit? How much more or less?

On the next page you will see one way your child might determine whether there is more or less money in the bank account.

NEXT

Ms. Scanlon's bank account has a deposit of $41.60 on Wednesday. She pays two bills for $17.05 and $26.55 on Thursday. Does Ms. Scanlon have more or less money in the account after the withdrawals than she did before the deposit? How much more or less?

You can start by rounding to estimate the change in the account balance. You could round to the nearest $1 or to the nearest $5.

Actual Amount	Round to the Nearest $1
41.60	42
−17.15	−17
−26.85	−27

Add the values rounded to the nearest $1.:

$$42 + (−17) + (−27) = −2$$

The estimate is −2. The change in the account is about −2, which indicates that Ms. Scanlon had less in her account after the withdrawals than she did before the deposit.

Calculate the change in the account using exact values.

$$41.60 + (−17.15) + (−26.85) = −2.40$$

Answer: The estimate tells you that Ms. Scanlon had about $2 less in her account after the withdrawals than she did before the deposit. You calculated the exact answer as $2.40. Your estimate of −$2 means −$2.40 is a reasonable solution.

Solve Problems with Rational Numbers

Name: _____

**Study the example showing how to add negative fractions.
Then solve problems 1–8.**

Example

Marita has a container of oatmeal. She uses $\frac{1}{4}$ cup of the oatmeal for breakfast and $\frac{3}{8}$ cup for a cookie recipe. What is the total change in the amount of oatmeal she has?

You can use a number line to represent this problem. Keep in mind that $\frac{1}{4}$ is equivalent to $\frac{2}{8}$.

1 Why are $\frac{1}{4}$ and $\frac{3}{8}$ represented with negative numbers on the number line in the example?

_____

_____

2 What do you need to do to $-\frac{1}{4}$ to locate it on a number

line that is measured in eighths?_____

3 You can also use an equation to solve the problem.
Complete the addition equation.

Change in oatmeal after breakfast	+	Change in oatmeal after cookie recipe	=	Total change
_____	+	_____	=	**?**

4 What is the total change in the number of
cups in the oatmeal container? Explain.

_____

Solve.

5 Nien has a flower farm. He cuts $4\frac{3}{4}$ square yards of flowers one day and $5\frac{2}{3}$ square yards of flowers the next. Use addition to find the total change in the square yards of flowers.

Show your work.

Solution: _____

6 Carl has a new bottle of laundry detergent. He uses 0.4 cup of laundry detergent while washing one load of laundry and 0.7 cup on another load. Use addition to find the total change in the number of cups of detergent in the bottle.

_____

7 What is the sum $-7\frac{1}{6} + 3\frac{5}{6}$ in simplest terms?

Show your work.

Solution: _____

8 At a recycling center, items are sorted and removed according to the material they are made out of. In one mixture of recycled materials, 2.625 tons of metal cans, 5.58 tons of paper, and some glass items are removed. If the total change in weight of the recycled materials is −9.5 tons, how many tons of glass were removed?

Show your work.

Solution: _____

Name: _____

Estimating with Decimals

Study the example showing how to use estimation when computing with positive and negative decimals. Then solve problems 1–9.

Example

The temperature at noon was 5.6°F. During the afternoon the temperature dropped 2.8°F and then dropped another 2.2°F in the evening. Estimate the new temperature.

You can use a number line to understand the problem by approximating, or *rounding,* each temperature to the nearest degree.

5.6 rounds up to 6.
2.8 rounds up to 3.
2.2 rounds down to 2.

Now, you can estimate the new temperature by finding 6 − 3 − 2. So, using estimation, the new temperature will be about 1°F.

---

1. Based on the estimate, do you think the actual new temperature will be above or below 0°F? Explain.

_____

2. Write and solve an equation to find the new temperature using exact values. What is the exact value of the new temperature?

_____

3. Peter got an exact new temperature of 11.6°F. Explain how Peter can use the estimate to determine that his answer is wrong. Then find and correct Peter's error.

_____

_____

4. Janet estimated to the nearest half degree before she found her exact answer. Is Janet's estimate more or less accurate than the estimate in the example problem? Explain.

_____

_____

Solve.

5 Kyle and Joan are estimating the total weight of three boxes that each weigh 14.62 pounds. Each student's estimate is shown below.

Kyle	Joan
3(15) = 45 lb	3(14.5) = 43.5 lb

Which estimate is more accurate? Explain how you know. Then find the actual total weight of the boxes.

_____

_____

6 Estimate 55.8 ÷ (−3.1). Then find the exact quotient.

Show your work.

Solution: _____

Use the following situation to solve problems 7–9.

Dusan had $49.60 in his checking account. He wrote one check for $24.40 and another check for $25.49.

7 Estimate the amount of money in Dusan's account after he wrote the checks.

_____

8 Explain why the estimate might not be enough information to show Dusan whether he has enough money in his checking account to cover the checks.

_____

_____

9 Dusan says that because he always rounds to the nearest dollar, he will always have more money in his account than his estimate. Is Dusan correct? Explain.

_____

Name: _____

Estimating with Fractions

Study the example showing how to use estimation when computing with positive and negative fractions. Then solve problems 1–6.

Example

A high diving board is about $9\frac{5}{6}$ feet above the water's surface. A diver jumps off the diving board and ends up $3\frac{1}{4}$ feet below the surface of the water. What is the total distance of the jump?

You can use rounding and a number line to help you estimate the answer.

Actual Distance	Nearest Integer
$9\frac{5}{6}$	10
$-3\frac{1}{4}$	−3

1 To the nearest integer, what is the distance of the jump?

_____

2 What is the exact distance of the jump?

Show your work.

Solution: _____

3 Compare the estimated distance of the jump to the actual distance? Is the actual distance reasonable?

_____

Lesson 8 Solve Problems with Rational Numbers

Solve.

4 Think about the problem $-6\frac{3}{5} - \left(-7\frac{4}{15}\right) + 2\frac{1}{5}$.

   a. Estimate the answer.

    _____

   b. Find the actual answer.

    _____

   c. Compare the estimate and the actual answer. Is your actual answer reasonable?

    _____

5 James baked $5\frac{1}{4}$ dozen peanut butter cookies and $4\frac{5}{6}$ dozen oatmeal cookies for a bake sale.

   a. Estimate the number of dozens of cookies he baked.

    _____

   b. Find the actual number of dozens of cookies he baked.

    _____

   c. How do the numbers compare? Is the actual number of dozens you found reasonable?

    _____

6 What is the smallest integer that makes the difference $x - \left(\frac{3}{4} + \frac{4}{5}\right)$ greater than 1? Use estimation to find the answer, and then find the exact difference to show that your answer is correct.

_____

_____

_____

_____

_____

_____

Name: _____

Solve Problems with Rational Numbers

Solve the problems.

1 Which expression is the best estimate of $1.25 + (-2.69)$?

A $1 + (-3)$ **C** $2 + (-3)$

B $1 + (-2)$ **D** $2 + (-2)$

Sue chose **B** as the correct answer. How did she get that answer?

How might a number line help you estimate decimals?

_____

_____

2 Which expression is the best estimate of $1\frac{1}{5} \times 3\frac{2}{3}$?

A 2×4

B 1×4

C 2×3

D 1×3

Should you round each value up or down?

3 The answer to which situation is best estimated by -7?

A The temperature falls 1.9°F from 4.3°F.

B A hot-air balloon rises 4.1 meters from the ground and then rises 2.3 meters more.

C A submarine goes 3.8 feet below the surface of the ocean and then goes 2.5 feet farther down.

D The amount of money Sarah has after she buys milk for $3.85 and bread for $2.45.

How can you estimate decimal amounts?

Solve.

4 Tell whether each statement is *True* or *False*.

   a. $-3\frac{3}{4} + 1 = -3\frac{2}{3} - (-1)$ ☐ True   ☐ False

   b. $2.855 - 1.375 = 1.48$ ☐ True   ☐ False

   c. $-12\frac{7}{12} + \left(-9\frac{5}{6}\right) = 3\frac{7}{12}$ ☐ True   ☐ False

   d. $6\frac{2}{5} - \left(-7\frac{1}{10}\right) = 13\frac{1}{2}$ ☐ True   ☐ False

Can you tell if the sum or difference will be positive or negative?

5 Justin earned $25.67 one week and $37.85 the next week. He also purchased a DVD for $19.99 and gas for his car for $22.07. He started with a zero balance in his checking account. Justin recorded all of these transactions in his checkbook and ended up with a balance of $105.58. Was his balance correct? If it was, write an equation to support the answer. If not, find the correct balance.

An estimate might help you determine whether Justin is correct.

_____

_____

_____

_____

6 Write a sum, difference, product, and quotient whose answers could all have an estimate of about 6. One expression should include only mixed numbers, one expression should include only decimals, one expression should include only negative rational numbers, and one expression should include only positive rational numbers.

When do you round a rational number up? When do you round a rational number down?

Sum: _____

Difference: _____

Product: _____

Quotient: _____

Unit 1 Game

Name: _____

Operation: Integers

What you need: Recording Sheet, 2 number cubes (1–6)

Directions

- Your goal is to create two integers and add or subtract them to reach one of the target numbers.

- To begin, each player rolls 2 number cubes and adds the numbers shown. These are the two target numbers, which can be positive or negative. Record both target numbers at the top of the Recording Sheet.

- For Round 1, both players roll a number cube and record the number next to the "0" in their Numbers column. Then roll the number cube again. Make the recorded number positive if you roll an even number. Otherwise, make it negative.

- Each player makes an addition or subtraction equation with 0 and his or her number. You may use the number line on the Recording Sheet to help you add or subtract. Record the sum or difference. If the result is equal to one of the target numbers, score 1 point.

- Write the result in the Numbers column, under the "0." This will be the first number in the equation for round 2.

- Play 9 more rounds. Start with the result from the previous round. Then roll to make another integer. Decide whether to add or subtract. Record the result, and score 1 point if it equals a target number.

- After 10 rounds, the player with the most points wins.

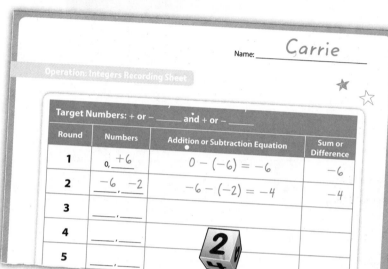

> I think about a number line when I add and subtract integers. What happens if I subtract a positive number? What if I subtract a negative number? What if I add a negative number?

Operation: Integers Recording Sheet

Target Numbers: + or − _____ and + or − _____			
Round	**Numbers**	**Addition or Subtraction Equation**	**Sum or Difference**
1	0, _____		
2	_____ , _____		
3	_____ , _____		
4	_____ , _____		
5	_____ , _____		
6	_____ , _____		
7	_____ , _____		
8	_____ , _____		
9	_____ , _____		
10	_____ , _____		

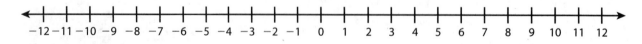

Score: _____ = _____
          Tally marks   Total

Name: _____

The Number System

In this unit you learned to:	Lesson
add and subtract positive and negative integers, for example: $-3 + (-4) = -7$.	1, 2, 3
multiply and divide positive and negative integers, for example: $-2 \cdot (-4) = 8$.	4
add and subtract rational numbers, for example: $-2.5 + 3.8 = 1.3$.	7
multiply and divide rational numbers, for example: $-\frac{1}{4} \div \frac{1}{3} = -\frac{3}{4}$.	6
solve word problems with rational numbers.	6, 7, 8

Use these skills to solve problems 1–8.

1 Which of the following equations are true? Select all that apply.

A $7 + (-7) = 14$

B $-4 + 9 = 5$

C $3 - (-10) = -7$

D $-2 - 6 = -8$

2 Which expression is equivalent to $5 - 14$? Select all that apply.

A $-3 \cdot 3$

B $9 \div (-1)$

C $-5 + 14$

D $14 - (-5)$

3 A football team loses 3 yards, gains 12 yards, gains 10 yards, and then loses 15 yards. Did the team gain yards or lose yards overall? How many yards?

Show your work.

Solution: _____

Solve.

4 Tell whether each fraction, $\frac{1}{n}$, is written as a terminating decimal or a repeating decimal for the given values of n. Write T for terminating or R for repeating.

n	2	3	4	5	6	8	9	10
Fraction								

5 Patrick recorded the daily changes of the value of a stock in dollars: −3.40, −8.09, −2.47, 1.86, and 3.55. What was the average daily change in the stock's value in dollars?

Show your work.

Solution: _____

6 A fish's position changes by −2.4 feet per second. How long will it take the fish to change its position by −13.2 feet?

A   0.18 seconds

B   5.5 seconds

C   10.8 seconds

D   31.68 seconds

7 A pelican flies $2\frac{1}{4}$ feet above the surface of the ocean. A dolphin swims $10\frac{1}{2}$ feet below the surface. How far apart are the dolphin and the pelican?

Show your work.

Solution: _____

_____

8 Given the four rational numbers below, find the greatest difference and the greatest product using two of the numbers for each operation.

$$2\frac{1}{3} \qquad 1.5 \qquad -1.25 \qquad -3\frac{1}{4}$$

Greatest difference: _____

_____

Greatest product: _____

_____

Name: _____

Answer the questions and show all your work on separate paper.

Mai and Wes played a board game. At the end of the game, each player had a negative balance in the bank. Mai's balance was the greater number, so she won the game.

Here are all the cards Mai and Wes picked during the game. They each picked the same number of cards.

Pay a $12 parking ticket.	Get $10 from your sister.	Find $8 in your jacket pocket.	Spend $32 on groceries.
Earn $6 from a rebate.	Buy a shirt for $14.	Spend $22 at the cinema.	Get $24 returning a product.
Earn $20 at a bake sale.	Earn $26 doing yard work.	Donate $20 to a charity.	Give your brother $2.
Lend a friend $12.	Receive a gift of $10.	Spend $18 on sporting goods.	Make $18 selling books.
Make $16 at a yard sale.	Donate $30 to a charity.	Buy office supplies for $8.	Receive a gift of $4.

> ## Checklist
>
> Did you . . .
> - ☐ match situations with positive and negative numbers?
> - ☐ try different combinations of numbers?
> - ☐ check your calculations?

Find the cards that Mai could have picked and the cards that Wes could have picked. Show the amount on each card as a positive or negative number. Then find each player's ending amount after picking all of the cards. Show all your work and tell how you know your solution is correct.

Reflect on Mathematical Practices

After you complete the task, choose one of the following questions to answer.

1 Persevere How did you decide which cards to use for each player?

2 Reason Mathematically How did you know whether a situation was represented by a positive or negative number?

Word Bank Here are some words that you might use in your answer.

positive	add	subtract
negative	sum	difference

Model Here is a model that you might use to find the solution.

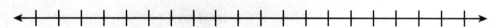

Sentence Starters Here are some sentence starters that might help you explain your work.

To add a negative number, _____

Some situations that are represented by negative numbers are _____

To compare negative numbers, _____

Unit 1 Vocabulary

My Examples

absolute value

the distance a number is from 0 on the number line

$$|2| = 2 \qquad |{-3}| = 3$$

My Words

_____

_____

_____

_____

_____

_____

_____

_____

_____

_____

My Words

My Examples

Dear Family,

Your child is learning about ratios expressed as complex fractions.

The ratio between two numbers is often written as a fraction. When one or both of the numbers being compared is a fraction, the ratio becomes a complex fraction (a fraction that contains another fraction). Your child is learning to interpret and simplify complex fractions to find unit rates and solve ratio problems.

When you know a unit rate, for example, the cost of one gallon of gas, you can then easily find the cost of several gallons. Unit rates also make it easy to compare costs of different items. Often, you need to calculate to find a unit rate.

Consider this situation:

To find the better buy, you need to figure out the price of 1 gallon for both choices. Then you can compare the unit rates.

The next page shows two different ways your child might find the unit rate for the smaller bottle.

Vocabulary

unit rate the numerical part of the rate, without the units. For a rate of $\frac{2}{5}$ dollar per apple, the unit rate is $\frac{2}{5}$.

complex fraction a fraction that contains another fraction.

example: $\frac{12}{\frac{3}{4}}$ or $\frac{\frac{1}{2}}{\frac{3}{4}}$

You want to know which size bottle of orange juice has a lower price per gallon.

- The larger bottle has a price of $4\frac{1}{2}$ dollars for 1 gallon.

- The smaller bottle has a price of $3\frac{3}{10}$ dollars for $\frac{3}{4}$ gallon.

To compare the prices, you need to find the unit price for the smaller bottle.

One way:

Write the ratio $3\frac{3}{10} : \frac{3}{4}$ as a fraction.

$$\frac{3\frac{3}{10}}{\frac{3}{4}}$$

Interpret the fraction as division.

$$\frac{33}{10} \div \frac{3}{4} = \frac{33}{10} \times \frac{4}{3}$$

Then simplify.

$$\frac{33}{10} \times \frac{4}{3} = \frac{44}{10}, \text{ or } 4\frac{4}{10}$$

Another way:

Use a double number line to show the relationship between fractions of a gallon and cost.

Have one number line show gallons, marked in fourths. The other number line shows cost, in fractions of a dollar.

- The cost for $\frac{3}{4}$ gallon is shown above the $\frac{3}{4}$ mark.

- Because $\frac{3}{4}$ is $\frac{1}{4} \times 3$, the cost for each $\frac{1}{4}$ gallon is a third of $3\frac{3}{10}$, or $1\frac{1}{10}$.

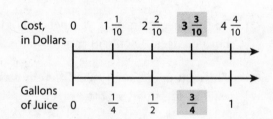

- So the cost of a whole gallon would be $1\frac{1}{10}$ more than $3\frac{3}{10}$, or $4\frac{4}{10}$.

Answer: Both methods show that the unit rate for the small bottle is $4\frac{4}{10}$, meaning that the cost of 1 gallon is \$4.40. The unit rate for the large bottle is \$4.50. The smaller bottle is a better buy.

Name: _Amanda S._

Ratios Involving Complex Fractions

Solve the problems.

1. A road sign gives drivers information about traffic on busy highways. One sign shows "15 miles in 20 minutes." What is this speed in miles per hour?

   Show your work.

   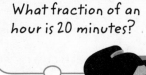

   Solution: _____

2. During a heavy rainstorm, a city in Florida received $12\frac{1}{4}$ inches of rain in $25\frac{1}{2}$ hours. What is the approximate rainfall rate in inches per hour?

   A about 2 inches per hour

   B about $\frac{1}{4}$ inch per hour

   C about 1 inch per hour

   D about $\frac{1}{2}$ inch per hour

3. Jeremy swims $5\frac{3}{5}$ kilometers in a 7-day period. He swims the same distance each day. What distance does he swim in a day?

   A $39\frac{1}{5}$ km C $\frac{4}{5}$ km

   B $1\frac{1}{5}$ km D $\frac{4}{35}$ km

   Eli chose **A** as the correct answer. How did he get that answer?

   _____

   _____

Solve.

4 Mrs. Cain's coleslaw recipe calls for $\frac{1}{3}$ cup of oil, $\frac{1}{2}$ cup of vinegar, and $\frac{1}{4}$ cup of sugar. Tell whether each statement is *True* or *False*.

Make sure the terms in each ratio are in the correct order.

a. The recipe uses $1\frac{1}{2}$ cups of oil for each cup of vinegar.　☐ True　☐ False

b. The recipe uses 2 cups of sugar for each cup of vinegar.　☐ True　☐ False

c. The recipe uses 2 cups of vinegar for each cup of sugar.　☐ True　☐ False

d. The recipe uses $\frac{2}{3}$ cup of oil for each cup of vinegar.　☐ True　☐ False

5 Fill in the table to show the amount of each ingredient needed to make different-size batches of coleslaw. Use the information from problem 4.

How can you use unit rates to solve the problem?

	Batch 1	Batch 2	Batch 3
Vinegar (cups)	1		
Oil (cups)		1	
Sugar (cups)			$\frac{3}{2}$

6 Rida and Elisa are each paid by the hour. Rida worked $5\frac{1}{2}$ hours and earned $77. Elisa worked $3\frac{3}{4}$ hours and earned $60. Whose hourly rate is greater?

Show your work.

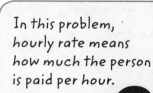

In this problem, hourly rate means how much the person is paid per hour.

Solution: _____

Dear Family,

Your child is learning about proportional relationships.

Here are some examples of proportional relationships that may be familiar to you.

- Tips left at a restaurant for service should be **proportional** to the total bill: *the greater the bill, the greater the tip.*

- The earnings of hourly employees are **proportional** to the number of hours worked: *working twice the number of hours earns twice the amount of money.*

- Ingredients of a recipe are **proportional** to one another: *you use the same proportions when making smaller or larger batches.*

Ratios compare two quantities. For example, the ratio "2 cups of flour to 1 cup of sugar" says that a recipe requires twice as much flour as sugar. A set of equivalent ratios represents a proportional relationship. The ratios below are all equivalent to the ratio 2 to 1, so they represent a proportional relationship.

$$\frac{2}{1} \quad \frac{4}{2} \quad \frac{6}{3} \quad \frac{8}{4} \quad \frac{10}{5}$$

Consider the following example:

Deon sees the chart below posted at the fruit stand:

Apples (lb)	2	5	10	15
Cost ($)	2.50	6.25	12.50	18.75

Is the cost proportional to the weight of apples purchased, or do you get a better deal if you buy more apples?

On the next page you will see two ways in which your child may determine whether there is a proportional relationship between weight and cost.

NEXT

How can you determine whether the cost is proportional to the weight?

Apples (lb)	2	5	10	15
Cost ($)	2.50	6.25	12.50	18.75

One way:
Find the ratio of dollars to pounds for each pair of values in the table. Then simplify to find the unit rate.

$$\frac{2.50}{2} = 1.25 \qquad \frac{6.25}{5} = 1.25 \qquad \frac{12.50}{10} = 1.25 \qquad \frac{18.75}{15} = 1.25$$

Because all of the ratios are equivalent, the cost is proportional to the weight of the apples purchased.

Another way:
Use a graph. Plot the pairs of values as ordered pairs on the coordinate plane and connect the points.

Because the graph is a straight line that goes through (0, 0), the relationship is proportional.

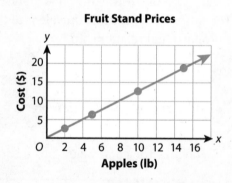

Answer: Both solutions show that the cost is proportional to the weight of apples purchased. The unit price is $1.25 per pound no matter how much you purchase.

Vocabulary

proportional relationship a numerical relationship that can be represented by equivalent ratios.

constant of proportionality the unit rate in a proportional relationship.

Understand
Proportional Relationships

Name: _____

> **Prerequisite: How do you find equivalent ratios?**

Study the example problem showing how to find equivalent ratios. Then solve problems 1–7.

Example

There are 3 counselors assigned to a group of 24 campers. At this rate, how many counselors are needed for 40 campers?

The given ratio is 24 campers to 3 counselors. That's a rate of 8 campers to 1 counselor. You can use this information to make a table of equivalent ratios.

Number of Campers	8	16	**24**	32	40
Number of Counselors	1	2	**3**	4	5

From the table you can see that 5 counselors are needed for 40 campers.

---

1 Explain how to use the unit rate to make the table in the example.

_____ THE UNIT RATE IS 8. THERE ARE 8 CAMPERS FOR EACH COUNSELOR._

_____ I THINK MULTIPLY 8 BY THE NUMBER OF COUNSELORS_

2 One ordered pair from the table is plotted on the coordinate plane. Finish plotting the ordered pairs.

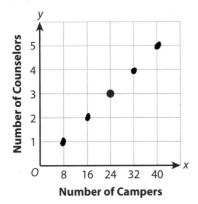

3 Suppose you had 9 counselors available. How many campers could you have?

_____

> ### Vocabulary
>
> **equivalent ratios**
> two or more ratios that are equal to one another.

Solve.

4 In 10 seconds, Jamal travels 550 feet on his bicycle. At this speed, how many feet can he travel in 1 minute? Explain.

_____

_____

_____

5 Cala uses 2 pounds of Feed-All fertilizer for a 100-foot row of vegetables at her farm. At this rate, how many pounds of fertilizer would she use for a 450-foot row of vegetables? Explain.

_____

_____

6 The directions for Grow Better fertilizer say that the 25-pound bag covers a 1,000-foot row of vegetables. Which brand would Cala need more of to fertilize her vegetables? Explain.

_____

_____

_____

7 Giselle has a catering business. There is a proportional relationship between the number of people and the amount of meat she uses for an event. The graph shows the amount of meat Giselle uses for 10 people. Find the amount of meat needed for 20, 30, 40, and 50 people. Finish labeling the graph and plotting ordered pairs. Finally, explain how to calculate the amount of meat needed for a party of 75 people.

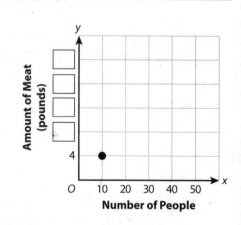

_____

_____

_____

Name: _____

Reason and Write

Study the example. Underline two parts that you think make it a particularly good answer and a helpful example.

Example

Describe a relationship involving some product or service and its cost that is NOT proportional. Explain how you know that it is not a proportional relationship.

Show your work. Use tables, graphs, words, and numbers to explain your answer.

Best Bike Rentals rents bikes by the day. The longer you rent the bike, the better their rate is. The table shows the cost of renting a bike for up to 7 days. The ratios of cost to days in this table are not equivalent because the relationship is not proportional.

Number of Days	1	2	3	4	5	6	7
Cost ($)	60	100	130	150	170	180	190

For example, $\frac{60}{1} = 60$, $\frac{100}{2} = 50$, and $\frac{130}{3} = 43\frac{1}{3}$. These three ratios are not equivalent. The rate of dollars per day is less the longer you keep the bike.

I can also plot the ordered pairs from the table on a coordinate grid.

The points cannot be connected with a straight line that goes through the origin. This is another way to show that the relationship is not proportional.

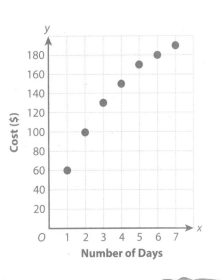

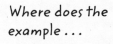

Where does the example . . .

- *answer both parts of the problem?*
- *use a table or graph to explain?*
- *use numbers to explain?*
- *use words to explain?*
- *give details?*

Solve the problem. Use what you learned from the model.

Describe a relationship involving some product or service and its cost that IS proportional. Explain why it is a proportional relationship, and identify the constant of proportionality.

Show your work. Use tables, graphs, words, and numbers to explain your answer.

Did you . . .

- answer both parts of the problem?

- use a table or graph to explain?

- use numbers to explain?

- use words to explain?

- give details?

Dear Family,

Your child is learning about equations for proportional relationships.

You might be familiar with proportional relationships if you have ever doubled or tripled the quantities in a recipe. Suppose that a recipe for soup calls for 3 cups of stock and 1 cup of vegetables. To double the recipe, you would use 6 cups of stock and 2 cups of vegetables.

There is a proportional relationship between the quantities in the original recipe and the quantities in the doubled recipe because $\frac{3}{1}$ is equivalent to $\frac{6}{2}$.

Suppose you wanted to make salad and salad dressing for a large gathering. You know that the dressing recipe calls for 3 times as much oil as vinegar. This proportional relationship can be represented with the equation below.

$$\text{quantity of oil} = 3 \cdot \text{quantity of vinegar}$$
$$\text{or}$$
$$y = 3x$$

The letters y and x in the equation stand for the proportional quantities of oil and vinegar in the dressing recipe.

Consider this situation:

Monty mixes red and yellow paint to make a certain shade of orange paint. For every 2 ounces of red paint, he needs 8 ounces of yellow paint. Identify the constant of proportionality and describe what it represents in this situation.

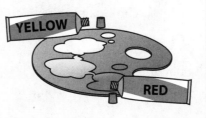

The next page shows three different ways your child may represent the proportional relationship to find the constant of proportionality.

NEXT

Monty mixes red and yellow paint to make orange paint. He uses 2 ounces of red paint for every 8 ounces of yellow paint. Use a table, a graph, and an equation to represent this proportional relationship. Identify the constant of proportionality and describe what it represents in this situation.

One way:
Use a table.

Yellow Paint (oz)	4	6	8	10	12	14	16
Red Paint (oz)	1	1.5	2	2.5	3	3.5	4

From the table you can see that for every 4 ounces of yellow paint you need 1 ounce of red paint. So the constant of proportionality is 4.

A second way:
Use a graph.

Graph the point (2, 8) and connect it to the point (0, 0). The point (1, 4) is on the line.

The constant of proportionality is the y-value of the point when the x-value is 1. The point (1, 4) on the graph shows that the constant of proportionality is 4.

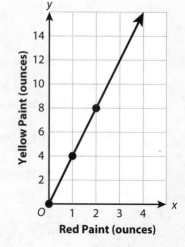

A third way:
Use an equation.

The ratio of yellow paint to red paint is $\frac{8}{2}$, so the constant of proportionality is $\frac{4}{1}$.

$$\begin{array}{c} \text{amount of} \\ \text{yellow paint} \end{array} = \begin{array}{c} \text{constant of} \\ \text{proportionality} \end{array} \cdot \begin{array}{c} \text{amount of} \\ \text{red paint} \end{array}$$

$$y = 4x$$

Answer: All three methods show that the constant of proportionality is 4, which means that Monty uses 1 ounce of red paint for every 4 ounces of yellow paint.

Name: _____

Write Equations for Proportional Relationships

Study the example showing how to identify a proportional relationship. Then solve problems 1–9.

Example

The table shows the relationship between the money that Leo earns and the number of lawns that he mows. Is the relationship proportional?

Number of Lawns	2	4	5	8
Money Earned ($)	10	20	25	40

The ratios of the money earned to the number of lawns all simplify to $\frac{5}{1}$, or 5, so the relationship is proportional.

1 Graph the relationship between the money earned and the number of lawns and connect the points. How does the graph tell you that the relationship is proportional?

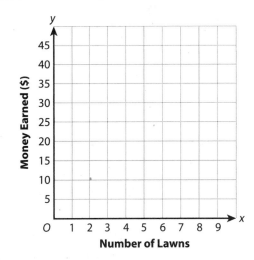

_____

_____

2 What does the ratio $\frac{5}{1}$ represent in terms of the example?

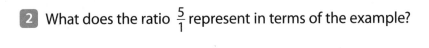

_____

_____

3 How can you use the graph to find the constant of proportionality? What is the constant of proportionality?

_____

4 Use the constant of proportionality to write an equation that represents the amount of money earned, y, for mowing x lawns. _____

5 If you know the constant of proportionality, m, for two proportional quantities, x and y, what equation can you write to describe the relationship?

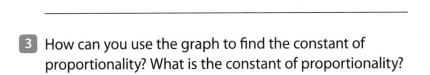

_____

Solve.

6 Nila uses the equation $c = 8h$ to figure out the total amount c she should charge a customer if she babysits for h hours. Find the constant of proportionality and explain what it means.

_____

7 Use the information in problem 6 to solve this problem. Nila decides to increase the rate she charges customers by $2 per hour. What equation should she now use to determine how much to charge her customers? Explain.

_____

8 The table shows the cost of several bunches of bananas. What equation can be used to represent the cost c of a bunch that weighs p pounds?

Number of Pounds	2.5	3.5	4	4.5
Cost ($)	1.05	1.47	1.68	1.89

Show your work.

Solution: _____

9 The graph shows the relationship between the distance that Dustin can drive his car and the amount of gas needed for that distance. Explain how Dustin can use the graph to predict the number of gallons of gas he will need for a trip of 120 miles. Then find the amount of gas he will need.

Show your work.

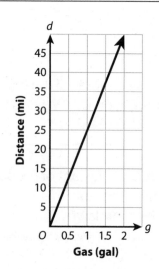

Solution: _____

Dear Family,

Your child is learning about problem solving with proportional relationships.

A percent is a common example of a proportional relationship. Here are some common situations involving percents that you may recognize.

- A store advertises a sale for 25% off the regular prices.

- A bank offers automobile loans with an interest rate of 4%.

- There is a 5% sales tax on an appliance purchase.

- A waiter receives a 15% tip on the amount of a restaurant bill.

- A salesperson earns an 18% commission on business equipment sales.

ercent is a rate per 100, and it can be expressed with the % symbol, fraction, or as a decimal.

$$25\% = \frac{25}{100} = 0.25$$

sider the following example:

s. Perez borrows $800 to buy a new mputer. She must pay back the total amount rrowed plus 7% simple interest in one year. hat amount will Ms. Perez pay back?

e next page you will see two different ways your child may ate the amount Ms. Perez will pay back.

Vocabulary

ple interest a percent of an amount borrowed that is paid to the er in addition to the amount borrowed.

mission a percent of a sales amount awarded to the person ng the sale.

Lesson 12 Problem Solving with Proportional Relationships

NEXT

> Ms. Perez borrows $800 to buy a new computer. She must pay back the total amount borrowed plus 7% simple interest in one year. What amount will she pay back?

To find the amount Ms. Perez will pay back, calculate the interest on the amount borrowed and add the interest to the amount borrowed.

One way:

Use a bar model.

Total Amount to Pay Back	
Amount Borrowed $800	Interest 7% of $800 for 1 year

The bar model shows that the total amount to pay back is equal to the amount borrowed, $800, plus the interest, 7% of $800. Remember you can write 7% as a decimal, 7% = 0.07.

$$800 + (0.07 \times 800) = 800 + 56 = 856$$

Another way:

Write an equation.

$$\text{Total to pay back} = \text{Amount borrowed} + \text{Amount of interest in 1 year}$$

$$t = 800 + (0.07 \times 800)$$

Solve the equation.

$$t = 800 + (0.07 \times 800)$$
$$= 800 + 56$$
$$= 856$$

Answer: Both methods show that $t = 856$, which means that Ms. Perez will pay back a total of $856 after one year.

Problem Solving with Proportional Relationships

Name: _____

Study the example showing how to write an equation for a proportional relationship. Then solve problems 1–6.

Example

Jamie is making bracelets using black and red beads. She uses 6 black beads for every 4 red beads. Represent the number of black beads for any given number of red beads using a table, a graph, and an equation. Identify the constant of proportionality.

The ratio of black beads to red beads will be the same for all quantities.

$$\frac{\text{black beads}}{\text{red beads}} = \frac{6}{4} = \frac{3}{2}$$

You can use this ratio to make a table.

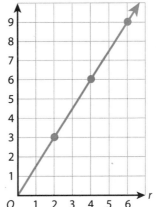

Red Beads, r	2	4	6
Black Beads, b	3	6	9

You can use the table to make a graph by plotting and connecting the ordered pairs. The constant of proportionality is $\frac{3}{2}$. This situation can be represented by the equation $b = \frac{3}{2}r$.

1 If Jaime uses 12 red beads, how many black beads does she use?

_____

2 If Jamie wants to maintain the relationship of black beads to red beads, could she make a bracelet with 5 red beads? Explain your answer.

_____

_____

_____

_____

Vocabulary

constant of proportionality the unit rate in a proportional relationship.

Solve.

3 Ana hikes at a constant speed. She travels 6 miles in 2 hours.

  a. Find her speed in miles per hour. Use it to write an equation for the distance, d, that Ana travels in h hours.

  _____

  b. Use the equation to find the distance Ana travels in 1.5 hours.

  _____

4 Mana is saving to buy a new bicycle. The equation $d = 12w$ represents the amount in dollars, d, that Mana saves in w weeks. What is the constant of proportionality? What does it represent in this situation?

_____

5 The table shows the number of gallons of water, g, that a water pump transfers in s seconds. How many gallons of water are pumped per second? What is an equation for the gallons of water, g, that the station can pump in s seconds?

Seconds, s	12	16	20
Gallons Pumped, g	9	12	15

Show your work.

  Solution: _____

_____

6 Joleen and Pablo want to fertilize a rectangular garden with an area of A square feet. They know that 5 cups of fertilizer will cover an area of 240 square feet. They each write an equation to represent the relationship between the area, A, and the number of cups of fertilizer, c.

Joleen's equation: $A = 48c$

Pablo's equation: $c = \frac{1}{48}A$

Which of the equations is correct? Explain how you know.

_____

_____

_____

Name: _____

Problem Solving with Percents

Study the example showing how to solve problems involving percents. Then solve problems 1–8.

Example

Tara buys a tablet that costs only $320 because it is on sale for 20% off the original price. Write an equation that you can use to find the original price, p, of the tablet.

You can use a bar model to help you understand the problem.

Original Price	
p	
Discounted Price $320 or 80% of Original Price	**Discount** 20% of Original Price

Tara pays 100% − 20%, or 80%, of the original price.

The discounted price is 80% of p, so $0.80p = 320$.

---

1 In the equation $0.80p = 320$, what do 0.80, p, and 320 represent?

_____

_____

2 Solve the equation $0.80p = 320$ to find the original price.

Show your work.

Solution: _____

3 The original price of the tablet that you found in problem 2 increases by 20%. Write an expression for finding the new price. What is the new price?

_____

Solve.

4 This year, a softball coach raised $1,200 for new equipment. That is 4% less than he raised last year. How much did he raise last year? Explain.

_____

_____

5 You buy a calculator for $65. A 6% sales tax is added. Write and solve an equation to find the total price, t.

_____

6 A store is having a sale with 10% off everything.

   a. Write an equation to show the sale price s of any item given its regular price r.

     _____

   b. Does your equation represent a proportional relationship? Explain.

     _____

     _____

7 A store owner buys cell phones for $40 and marks up the price by 25%. Explain how to find the price at which she sells the cell phones.

_____

_____

8 A video game that usually costs $50 is on sale for $32.50. What percent of the regular price is the discount?

Show your work.

Solution: _____

Vocabulary

tax a percent of a purchase that is added to the purchase and paid to a government.

markup a percent of the cost of an item that is added to the cost to determine the item's selling price.

Dear Family,

Your child is learning about proportional relationships involving percent increase and decrease.

A percent is often used to describe how an amount or quantity changes. Here are some examples of *percent increases* and *percent decreases*.

- A retailer's sales increased by 45% from the previous year.

- A newscast reports gasoline prices are 30% lower than last year.

- A county increases property taxes by 5%.

- A city transit system announces a fare increase of 8%.

- A census report finds that the population of a state decreased by 15% over the past decade.

A percent is also used to describe the amount of error in a calculation. For example, a runner may estimate how long it takes to run a distance but may actually run the distance in a longer amount of time. The ratio of how far off the estimate is from the actual time compared to the actual time is called the *percent error*.

Consider this situation:

A computer-support employee at a company handled an average of 25 calls each day in one month. The next month, she handled an average of 40 calls each day. What is the percent increase in the average number of calls handled each day from one month to the next?

The next page shows two different ways your child might find the percent increase in the number of calls the employee handled.

NEXT

A computer-support employee handled an average of 25 calls each day in one month and an average of 40 calls each day the next month. What is the percent increase in the average number of calls she handled?

One way:

Use a bar model. Compare the amount of change in the number of calls to the original number of calls.

Original amount	5	5	5	5	5
Amount of change	5	5	5		

$x\%$ 100%

The original number of calls is 25. The amount of change is $40 - 25$, or 15.

The bar model shows that the ratio of the amount of change to the original amount is equal to the ratio of x to 100.

$$\frac{15}{25} = \frac{x}{100} \longrightarrow \frac{3}{5} = \frac{x}{100} \longrightarrow 60 = x$$

An increase from 25 to 40 calls is a percent increase of 60%.

Another way:

Use a proportion. Find the amount of change and compare it to the original amount. This ratio is equal to the percent change, which in this case is a percent increase.

$$\frac{40 - 25}{25} = \frac{x}{100} \longrightarrow \frac{15}{25} = \frac{x}{100} \longrightarrow \frac{3}{5} = \frac{x}{100} \longrightarrow 60 = x$$

An increase from 25 to 40 calls is a percent increase of 60%.

Answer: Both methods show that an increase from 25 to 40 calls is a percent increase of 60%, which means that the employee handled 60% more calls on average each day in one month than in the previous month.

Proportional Relationships

Name: _____

Study the example problem showing how to solve a problem with percents. Then solve problems 1–7.

Example

Chumani has a coupon for 15% off the total bill at a new restaurant. Her original bill is $32.00. After the discount, what amount is her bill?

First, find the amount of the discount.

15% = 0.15 and 0.15 × 32 = $4.80

Subtract the discount from the original amount.

$32.00 − $4.80 = $27.20

So Chumani's bill is $27.20.

1 A bar model can also be used to represent the problem. Complete the bar model.

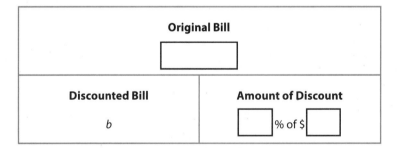

2 Write and solve an equation to represent the relationship shown in the bar model.

_____

3 The percent of the discount in the problem above is 15%. What percent of the original bill is Chumani's bill? How could you solve the problem using this percent?

_____

_____

Solve.

4 Chander earns a base pay of $2,200 per month. He also earns a commission of 4% of his total sales. One month Chander earned $2,400. Explain how to find Chander's total sales for that month. How much were his total sales?

_____

_____

_____

5 Marian borrowed money to buy a sound system that costs $450. She is charged 5% simple interest for one year. What is the total amount that she pays for the sound system if she pays the full amount in one year?

Show your work.

Solution: _____

6 Dan paid $34.30 for a sweater. The price included a 40% markup. Find the cost of the sweater before the markup was added.

Show your work.

Solution: _____

7 A jacket that originally sold for $60.00 was on sale for 10% off. When it didn't sell after several weeks, the sale price was discounted another 40% off the discounted price. What was the final price of the jacket? Is the total discount equal to 50%? Explain.

_____

_____

_____

Name: _____

Finding Percent Change

Study the example problem showing how to find percent change. Then solve problems 1–7.

Example

The plants that Loma grew for her science project averaged 6 inches in height. Two weeks later, the plants averaged 9 inches in height. What was the percent increase in the average height of the plants?

You can use a bar model to compare the original height to the change in height.

original height

change in height

$x\%$ 100%

You can also use the proportion below to compare the change to the original amount.

$$\frac{\text{amount of change}}{\text{original amount}} = \text{percent change}$$

$$\frac{9 - 6}{6} = \frac{x}{100}$$

---

1 Use either the bar model or the proportion to solve for x. What was the percent increase in the average height of the plants?

_____

2 Would the percent change be *greater than* or *less than* 50% if the plants had grown to 8 inches instead of 9?

_____

3 After 4 weeks, the height of the plants had grown from 6 inches to 12 inches. Write and solve a proportion to find the percent increase in the height of the plants.

_____

_____

Solve.

4 Students donated 2,500 cans of food to the local food pantry last year. They donated 4,000 cans this year. What is the percent increase in the number of cans donated?

Show your work.

Solution: _____

5 Mike plays basketball. He attempted 32 free throws in January and 28 free throws in February.

a. Is the percent change a *percent increase* or a *percent decrease*? _____

b. Write and solve a proportion to find the percent change in the number of free throws.

Show your work.

Solution: _____

6 Find the percent of increase or decrease.

a. x to $5x$ _____

b. $2.5y$ to $1.5y$ _____

c. n to $\frac{4}{5}n$ _____

d. $3.2t$ to $5.2t$ _____

7 A store manager pays $40 for a shirt and adds a markup of 20%. During a store sale, the manager marks the cost of the shirt down by 20%. What is the percent of change from the original cost, $40, to the sale price?

_____

_____

Name: _____

Percent Error

Study the example problem showing how to find percent error. Then solve problems 1–8.

Example

A thermometer manufacturer compares the reading on one of its thermometers to a thermometer that they know is accurate. The accurate thermometer reads 25°C. Their thermometer reads 30°C. What is the percent error in their thermometer's reading?

You can use a bar model to help you understand the problem.

You can also use a proportion.

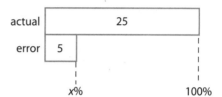

$$\frac{\text{amount of error}}{\text{actual amount}} = \frac{x}{100}$$

$$\frac{30 - 25}{25} = \frac{x}{100}$$

---

1. Use either the bar model or the proportion to solve for x. What is the percent error in the thermometer's reading?

   _____

   _____

2. Explain the relationship between the x in the bar model and the x in the proportion.

   _____

3. The reading on a different thermometer is 23°C. Do you think the percent error of this thermometer is more or less than for the first thermometer? Explain your answer.

   _____

4. Find the percent error of a thermometer reading of 23°C. _____

Solve.

5 At the school carnival, students are asked to guess the number of marbles in a jar to win a prize. There are 240 marbles in the jar. The closest guess is 280 marbles. What is the percent error of the guess? Explain. Round your answer to the nearest percent.

_____

_____

6 Kai needed to cut 25 inches from a long board. He accidently cut 24 inches from the board. What is his percent error? Explain.

_____

7 Bev weighs a bag of apples labeled 5 pounds and finds that the weight is actually 72 ounces. To the nearest percent, what is the percent error in the weight? (1 pound = 16 ounces)

Show your work.

Solution: _____

8 Semira did a physics activity during which she rolled toy cars down a ramp and measured the distance each car traveled. On one trial, the actual distance that the car traveled was 75 cm. Semira's measurement was too short and had a 12% error. What was her distance measurement?

Show your work.

Solution: _____

Name: _____

Proportional Relationships

Solve the problems.

1 For each of the following situations, is the percent of change between 20% and 30%?

Select *Yes* or *No* for each situation.

a. A $12 cost increases to $15. ☐ Yes ☐ No

b. A boy's height increases from 52 inches to 61 inches. ☐ Yes ☐ No

c. The temperature falls from 3°F to 2°F. ☐ Yes ☐ No

Which value goes in the denominator when you calculate a percent of change?

2 A customer pays $18 for a DVD that originally cost $20. What is the percent decrease in the cost of the DVD?

A 2%

B 10%

C 11%

D 18%

Barbara chose **C** as the correct answer. How did she get that answer?

_____

_____

_____

What is the change in the cost of the DVD?

3 Brady needs to cut a piece of scrapbook paper 12 centimeters long. He cuts pieces of the following lengths. Which cut results in a percent error of 15%? Select all that apply.

A 10.2 centimeters

B 11.2 centimeters

C 13.8 centimeters

D 18.0 centimeters

A diagram might help you solve this problem.

Solve.

4 Jasmine sells beaded jewelry. She calculates the price at which she sells the jewelry by adding a percent markup to the amount it costs her to make the jewelry. Complete the following table. Record money amounts to the nearest cent and markups to the nearest whole percent.

How does a markup affect the original cost?

Show your work.

Type of Jewelry	Cost to Make ($)	Percent Markup (%)	Selling Price ($)
Bracelet	7.69	40	
Necklace	8.66		12.56

5 In the late 1980s, there were only 22 California condors, which are large predatory birds, living in the wild. In 2012, the population had increased to 405 condors. To the nearest whole percent, what is the percent increase in the California condor population?

What is the change in the number of California condors?

Show your work.

Solution: _____

6 The manufacturer of an oven states that the temperatures displayed while cooking are within a 5% error. Rachel is using the oven to cook a chocolate cake that must be cooked at a temperature below 325°F. The oven display shows a temperature of 310°F. Can Rachel be certain that the temperature is suitable for cooking her cake? Explain your answer.

What is the ratio of the amount of error to the highest temperature?

_____

_____

_____

Rolling Ratios

What you need: Recording Sheet, 3 number cubes
(2 labeled 1–6 and 1 labeled 4, 6, 8, 9, 10, 12)

Directions

- Your goal is to plot two points that represent a proportional relationship on each coordinate grid on the Recording Sheet.

- Take turns. Roll all three number cubes. Pick two of them to make an ordered pair. You may choose to roll one, two, or all three of the number cubes again before picking two numbers.

- Name the ordered pair that you will plot. You can plot the ordered pair on any grid that is blank. You can also plot it on a grid that already has a point if the numbers in both ordered pairs form equivalent ratios. If you cannot plot the ordered pair, your turn ends.

- When you have plotted two ordered pairs on a grid, draw a line and write an equation to represent the proportional relationship.

- Continue until one player has graphed four proportional relationships.

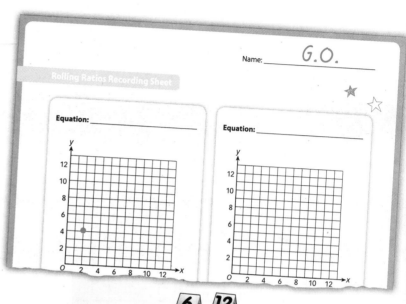

I can plot a point at (6, 12) on the same grid with the point (2, 4). The numbers in each ordered pair form a ratio that is equivalent to $\frac{2}{1}$. The equation would be $y = 2x$.

Name: _____

Equation: _____

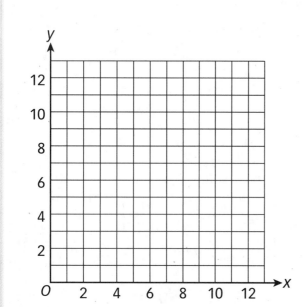

Equation: _____

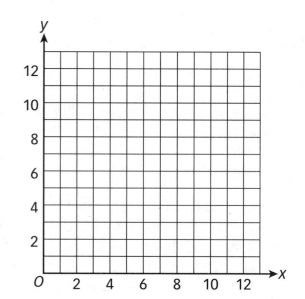

Equation: _____

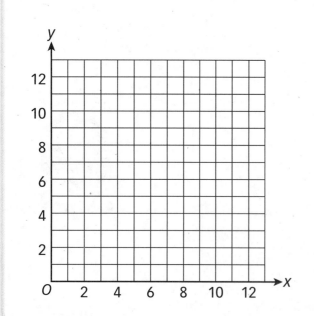

Equation: _____

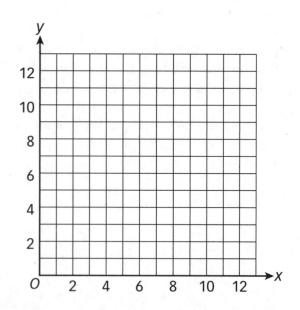

Name: _____

Ratios and Proportional Relationships

In this unit you learned to:	Lesson
find unit rates with complex fractions, for example: $\frac{1}{4}$ cup oats per $\frac{1}{2}$ cup flour $= \frac{1}{2}$ cup oats per 1 cup flour.	9
identify proportional relationships and the constant of proportionality.	10
graph proportional relationships.	10
interpret equations and graphs of proportional relationships.	11
solve multi-step percent problems involving tax, tips, markups, etc., for example: $5.00 + 5\%$ tax $= 5 \times 1.05 = \$5.25$.	12
solve multi-step percent problems involving percent change or percent error.	13

Use these skills to solve problems 1–8.

1 Janelle can walk $3\frac{3}{4}$ miles in $1\frac{1}{2}$ hours. At this rate, how many miles can Janelle walk in 4 hours?

_____

_____

2 You give a delivery driver $15.50 for a pizza that costs $12.50. You tell the driver to keep the change as a tip. Is the tip *more* than or *less* than 20%?

_____

3 One week Anil earned $4 per hour. The next week he earned $4.50 per hour. What was the percent increase in his hourly rate?

A 0.5%

B 11%

C 12.5%

D 89%

4 Which expression CANNOT be used to calculate the sale price of a fish tank that was originally priced at *d* dollars and is on sale for 25% off? Select all that apply.

A $d - 0.25d$

B $1.25d$

C $0.75d$

D $1.7d$

Solve.

5 Does the equation represent a proportional relationship? Select *Yes* or *No*.

a. $y = 4x$ ☐ Yes ☐ No

b. $y = 4x + 3$ ☐ Yes ☐ No

c. $y = \frac{1}{2}x$ ☐ Yes ☐ No

d. $y = \frac{1}{2}x - 5$ ☐ Yes ☐ No

6 A store sells packages of 3 pens for $1.50, 8 pens for $4.00, and 12 pens for $6.00. Let *c* represent the total cost and *p* represent the number of pens. Write an equation to represent this situation.

_____

7 A principal estimated that 400 people attended the performance of the school play. After counting the tickets, he found that 423 people attended. What was the percent error in the principal's estimate?

Show your work.

Solution: _____

8 The point $\left(5\frac{5}{8}, 2\frac{1}{4}\right)$ lies on a line that represents a proportional relationship.

Part A

Write an equation for this relationship. What is the constant of proportionality?

_____

Part B

The point $\left(6\frac{1}{2}, y\right)$ also lies on the line. What is the *y*-coordinate of the point?

_____

Name: _____

Answer the questions and show all your work on separate paper.

You have been asked to make snack mix for a school event. Below are the main ingredients for two popular recipes. The amounts are for 1 serving.

Nutty Snack Mix	**Granola Snack Mix**
$\frac{3}{8}$ ounce almonds	$\frac{3}{4}$ ounce granola
$\frac{1}{4}$ ounce peanuts	$\frac{1}{2}$ ounce dried fruit

Below is information about bulk products you can buy at the local market.

- Almonds cost $9 per pound.
- The price of peanuts is $6 per pound.
- Granola costs $5.25 per pound. Take 10% off the total cost if you buy more than 2 pounds.
- The price of mixed dried fruit is $5 per pound.

The total number of guests has not yet been determined, but you need to get some estimates of what the costs might be.

Here is what you need to do:

- Choose which recipe to make and explain why you made this choice.
- Find the amounts of ingredients needed for 25, 50, 100, 150, and 200 servings.
- The maximum number of guests is 200. Make a shopping list and determine the cost to make the snack mix for the maximum number of guests.

Reflect on Mathematical Practices

1 **Make Sense of Problems** What was the first step that you took in completing the task? Why?

2 **Use Models** Explain why you chose a graph or a table for showing the amounts of ingredients needed for different numbers of servings.

Word Bank Here are some words that you might use in your answer.

ratio	per	ounce
proportional relationship	unit rate	pound

Models Here are some models that you might use to find the solution.

Servings						
Ingredient						
Ingredient						

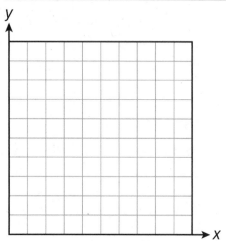

Sentence Starters Here are some sentence starters that might help explain your work.

I decided to _____

The ratio of _____

The cost per pound _____

The total cost _____

Name: _____

My Examples

rate

the ratio that compares the first quantity to one unit of the second quantity; for a ratio of 2 dollars for every 5 apples, the rate is $\frac{2}{5}$ dollars per apple

unit rate

the numerical part of the rate, without the units; for a rate of $\frac{2}{5}$ dollar per apple, the unit rate is $\frac{2}{5}$

equivalent ratios

two or more ratios that are equal to one another

proportional relationship

the relationship among a group of ratios that are equivalent

constant of proportionality

the unit rate in a proportional relationship

simple interest

a percent of an amount borrowed
(or invested) that is paid to the lender
(or investor) in addition to the
original amount

My Words

_____

_____

_____

_____

_____

_____

_____

Dear Family,

> **Your child is learning how to write equivalent linear expressions.**

Many situations in real life can be represented as mathematical expressions. For example, suppose the price of a movie ticket is x dollars and the price of popcorn is y dollars. The expression $x + y$ represents the cost of one ticket and one popcorn. You can find the cost of two tickets and two popcorns in a few different ways.

$$\left. \begin{array}{l} x + y + x + y \\ 2x + 2y \\ 2(x + y) \end{array} \right\}$$ Each expression represents the cost of 2 tickets and 2 popcorns.

The three expressions $x + y + x + y$, $2x + 2y$, and $2(x + y)$ are equivalent expressions because they all represent the same cost.

Consider the following example:

A neighborhood group is replacing a fence around a rectangular community garden. The length of the  garden is 4 times its width. Write three different expressions that you can use to describe the perimeter of the community garden.

On the next page you will see three different expressions your child might write to describe the perimeter of the garden.

Vocabulary

equivalent expressions expressions that have the same value for every value of the variable or variables.

Lesson 14 Equivalent Linear Expressions   **139**

A fence around a rectangular community garden is being replaced. The garden is 4 times as long as it is wide. Write three different expressions that you can use to describe the perimeter of the community garden.

You can make a diagram of the garden and label its length and width to help write expressions to describe the perimeter.

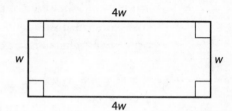

One expression:
Write an expression to show the perimeter as the sum of all four sides of the rectangle.

$4w + w + 4w + w$

A second expression:
Write an expression to show the perimeter as the sum of twice the length and twice the width of the rectangle.

$2(4w) + 2w$

A third expression:
Write an expression to show the perimeter as twice the sum of the length and the width of the rectangle.

$2(4w + w)$

To show that the three expressions are equivalent, simplify each expression.

$4w + w + 4w + w = 10w$
$2(4w) + 2w = 8w + 2w = 10w$
$2(4w + w) = 8w + 2w = 10w$

Answer: The three expressions, $4w + w + 4w + w$, $2(4w) + 2w$, and $2(4w + w)$, all represent the perimeter of the garden. They all simplify to the same expression, $10w$, so all three expressions are equivalent expressions.

Equivalent Linear Expressions

Solve the problems.

---

1 Which expression is equivalent to $3n + 2(1 - 4n)$?

To simplify this expression, what should you do first?

A $2 - n$ **C** $2 + 11n$

B $2 - 5n$ **D** $2 - 11n$

Samuel chose **A** as the correct answer. How did he get that answer?

A IS THE CORRECT ANSWER BECAUSE SAMUEL MULTIPLIED

2 w/ 1 AND NOT WITH THE 4n.

---

2 The width of a rectangle is represented by $5 + 2y$.
The length is twice as long as the width. What is the
perimeter of the rectangle? Select all correct expressions.

A diagram might help you solve this problem.

A $4(5 + 2y)$

B $6(5 + 2y)$ $5 + 2y$ [rectangle] $5 + 2y$

C $20 + 8y$

D $30 + 12y$ A, C

---

3 The length of one side of a square field is represented by
the expression $3 - 7x$.

How do you find the perimeter of a square?

a. Write an expression for the perimeter of the field
expressed as a sum.

b. What is an expression for the perimeter of the field
expressed as a product?

c. Use the distributive property to write the product in
part (b) as an equivalent expression.

Solve.

4 Tell whether each statement is *True* or *False*.

a. $2(3 - 4y) = 6 - 4y$ ☐ True ☑ False

b. $3 + 5(9 + 2n) = 48 + 5n$ ☐ True ☑ False

c. $9 - 3(y - 2) = 3 - 3y$ ☑ True ☐ False

d. $3(6x - 2) - 7 = 18x - 13$ ☑ True ☐ False

How do you know when expressions are equivalent?

5 The expression $24y + 36$ represents the cost of a dozen eggs. Use factoring to write an expression that is equivalent to $24y + 36$. Then write an expression for the cost of one egg.

How do you factor an expression?

_____

6 Roberto examines several geometric figures. The length of each side of each figure is $(2d - 7)$ feet. Using the following table, write the number of sides and two different expressions for the perimeter of each figure.

The prefix of the figure name indicates the number of sides in the figure.

Figure	Number of Sides	Perimeter Expression 1	Perimeter Expression 2
Pentagon	5	5a	S+S+S+S+S
Octagon	8	8a	S+S+S+S+S +S+S +S
Triangle	3	3a	S+S+S
Hexagon	6	6a	S+S+S+S+S +S
Square	4	4a	S+S+S+S

7 Use the distributive property to find an expression that is equivalent to $2(x + 7) - (3x + 1)$.

Show your work.

You will need to distribute –1 to find the answer.

Solution: _____

©Curriculum Associates, LLC Copying is not permitted.

Dear Family,

Your child is learning about writing linear expressions.

Your child has already learned that you can use linear expressions to describe many situations and that some linear expressions are equivalent.

Now your child is learning to write linear expressions. You can represent a situation with different linear expressions. The expression that you write depends on how you interpret the situation. Look at the following examples.

The sale price of an item is 35% off the regular price. You can think about the sale price in different ways:

- the regular price minus 35% of the regular price

- 65% of the regular price

A customer pays 6% sales tax on the price of an item. You can think about the total amount paid in different ways:

- price of the item plus 6% of the price

- 106% of the price

Consider this situation:

A winter coat is on sale for 40% off. The original price of the coat is $89.95. Write two different expressions that represent the sale price of the coat. Use each expression to calculate the sale price of the coat.

The next page shows two different expressions your child may write to find the sale price of the coat.

NEXT ▷

A winter coat is on sale for 40% off. The original price of the coat is $89.95. Write two different expressions that represent the sale price. Use each expression to calculate the sale price of the coat.

Your child may use a bar diagram to represent the situation.

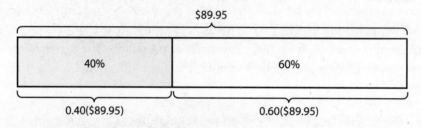

$89.95

| 40% | 60% |

0.40($89.95)   0.60($89.95)

The whole bar represents the original price of the coat. The shaded section represents the 40% discount. The unshaded section represents 60% of the original price of the coat.

One way: Think of the sale price as the original price minus the discount, which is 40% of the original price. So subtract the 40% discount from the original price.

sale price = original price − discount
sale price = original price − 40% of original price
$$= 89.95 - 0.40(89.95)$$
$$= 89.95 - 35.98$$
$$= 53.97$$

Another way: Think of the sale price as 100% − 40% = 60% of the original price. So find 60% of the original price.

sale price = 60% of the original price
$$= 0.60 \times 89.95$$
$$= 53.97$$

Answer: The different methods show different expressions you can use to find the sale price of the coat. The expressions 89.95 − 0.40(89.95) and 0.60(89.95) can both be used to find that the sale price is $53.97.

Dear Family,

Your child is learning about solving problems with equations.

You can solve some word problems using reasoning and arithmetic or by writing an equation to represent the situation. For example, consider the following situation.

Suppose 10 people attend a concert and spend a total of $140 on tickets and souvenirs. Tickets are $10 each and souvenirs are $5 each. How many souvenirs are purchased?

You can solve the problem using arithmetic or an equation.

Arithmetic	Equation
10 tickets × $10 per ticket = $100 $140 total spent − $100 for tickets = $40 $40 ÷ $5 per souvenir = 8 souvenirs	Let s be the number of souvenirs. $10(10) + 5s = 140$ $100 + 5s = 140$ $5s = 40$ $s = 8$

Knowing how to solve equations involving variables will help your child solve more complex word problems.

Consider the following example:

Kara joined a city bike-share program. Membership is $20 per month. Kara can use the bikes an unlimited number of times for 30 minutes or less at no additional cost. If she needs to use a bike for longer than 30 minutes, it costs an additional $7.50 each time. Kara paid $42.50 for the bike-share program last month. How many times did she use a bike for longer than 30 minutes last month?

On the next page you will see two different ways your child might solve the problem.

NEXT

Lesson 16 Solve Problems with Equations

Membership in a bike-share program is $20 per month. Kara can use the bikes an unlimited number of times for 30 minutes or less at no additional cost, but it costs $7.50 each time she uses a bike for longer than 30 minutes. Kara paid $42.50 for the bike-share program last month. How many times did she use a bike for longer than 30 minutes last month?

One way: Use arithmetic to solve the problem.

Kara's cost for last month: $42.50
Monthly cost of bike-share membership: $20.00
Total cost for using a bike longer than 30 minutes.
   $42.50 − $20.00 = $22.50

You can find the number of times Kara used a bike for longer than 30 minutes by dividing the total cost by the cost per use.
   $22.50 ÷ $7.50 = 3

Kara used a bike for longer than 30 minutes 3 times.

Another way: Write and solve an equation.

Let b represent the number of times Kara used a bike for longer than 30 minutes.

membership + (cost of each • (number of = total cost
                     longer use)   longer uses)

   20   +   7.50   •   b   = $42.50

To find the value of b, get b by itself on one side of the equation.

$$20 + 7.5b = 42.5$$
$$20 - 20 + 7.5b = 42.5 - 20$$
$$7.5b = 22.5$$
$$7.5b \div 7.5 = 22.5 \div 7.5$$
$$b = 3$$

Kara used a bike for longer than 30 minutes 3 times.

Answer: Whether you use arithmetic or an equation, the result is 3, meaning that Kara used a bike for longer than 30 minutes 3 times.

Name: _AMANDA S._

Solve Two-Step Problems with Fractions

Study the example showing how to solve two-step problems that involve fractions. Then solve problems 1–8.

Example

The perimeter of the triangle shown is 20 inches. Write an expression for the perimeter. Then write an equation that you can use to find the length of each side.

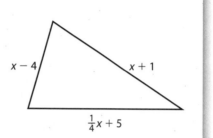

Perimeter: $(x - 4) + (x + 1) + \left(\frac{1}{4}x + 5\right) = \frac{9}{4}x + 2$

Equation: $\frac{9}{4}x + 2 = 20$

---

1 In the example, explain how the term $\frac{9}{4}x$ was obtained in the expression for the perimeter.

_____ ADDING x AND $\frac{1}{4}$ x _____

2 To find the value of x in the equation $\frac{9}{4}x + 2 = 20$, you first get the term with x by itself on one side of the equation. How can you do that? What equation do you then have?

_____ SUBTRACT 2 FROM BOTH SIDES _____

3 How can you find the value of x in the equation you wrote for problem 2? What is the value of x?

_____ MULTIPLY THE 2 SIDES BY THE RECIPRICAL & COEFFICIENT VARIABLE _____

4 Find the length of each side of the triangle. Check that the perimeter is equal to 20 inches.

Show your work.

Solution: _____ LENGTHS - 4, 7, & 9 _____

Solve.

5 Solve the equation $\frac{2}{5}x - 1 = 9$. Complete each step of the solution and check your solution.

$$\frac{2}{5}x - 1 = 9$$

$$\frac{2}{5}x - 1 \rule{2cm}{0.4pt} = 9 \rule{1.5cm}{0.4pt}$$

$$\frac{2}{5}x = \rule{2cm}{0.4pt}$$

$$\frac{2}{5}x \rule{2cm}{0.4pt} = \rule{2cm}{0.4pt}$$

$$x = \rule{2cm}{0.4pt}$$

Check: _____

6 Paco says that the solution to $\frac{2}{5}x - 1 = 9$ is $x = 4$.

Do you agree? Explain.

_____ X= 4   THERE WAS NO SOLUTION _____

7 The width of a rectangle is two-thirds of the length. The perimeter of the rectangle is 15 centimeters. What is the length, ℓ, of the rectangle? Explain.

_____ ANSWER - $1\frac{9}{2}$ $2\left(d + \frac{2}{3}d\right) = 15$ _____

_____

8 You buy $1\frac{1}{4}$ yards of fabric and an $8 clothing pattern.

Your total cost with a 6% sales tax added is $18.55. What is the cost per yard of the fabric?

Show your work.

Solution: _____ THE COST PER YARD IS $7.6 _____

Name: AMANDA

Solve Multi-Step Problems with Decimals

Study the example showing how to solve multi-step problems that involve decimals. Then solve problems 1–9.

Example

Olga buys tickets to a concert. She pays $27.75 for each ticket plus a handling fee of $5.50 for the order. The total cost is $144.25. How many tickets, n, did Olga buy?

You can use an equation to solve the problem.

Cost of tickets + Handling fee = Total cost

$$27.75n \quad + \quad 5.50 \quad = 144.25$$

1 What does n represent in the problem?

HOW MANY TICKETS OLGA BOUGHT

2 What does $27.75n$ represent? Explain.

COST OF EACH TICKET. SUBTRACT 5.50 ON BOTH SIDES & DIVIDE

THE $n = 5$.

3 How much did Olga pay for the tickets without the handling fee? Explain how you know.

22.20

4 When solving the equation $27.75n + 5.50 = 144.25$, what can you do to get $27.75n$ by itself on one side of the equation? What is the result?

5 How can you solve the simplified equation that you wrote in problem 3? Solve the equation.

Solve.

6 Solve the equation $18.2 + 1.5x = 37.7$.

a. How can you get $1.5x$ by itself on one side of the equation? Do this first step to start to solve the equation.

$1.5x = 22.5$

b. How could you use the result of part (a) to find the value of x?

DIVIDE $\dfrac{22.5}{1.5}$

7 Solve the equation $0.04x - 3.82 = 0.68$.

Show your work.

Solution: $x = 112.5$

8 Solve the equation $8.5 - 1.2x = 6.7$.

Show your work.

Solution: $x = 1.5$

9 Nita simplified the equation in problem 8 to $1.8 = 1.2x$. How did she get that? Is this a valid way to solve the equation? Explain.

SUBTRACT 8.5 FROM BOTH SIDES OF THE EQUATION THEN DIVIDE BY

-1.

Dear Family,

> **Your child is learning about solving problems with inequalities.**

An equation uses an equal sign (=) to show that two expressions are equivalent. An inequality uses inequality symbols to show the relationship between two expressions. The inequality symbols are greater than (>), greater than or equal to (≥), less than (<), and less than or equal to (≤).

Here are some examples of inequalities.

$5 < 12$ 5 is less than 12.

$\frac{1}{2}r > 55$ $\frac{1}{2}$ times r is greater than 55.

You can use inequalities to represent situations in everyday life. Consider this example:

> *Ms. Ruiz has a family cell phone plan. The plan includes 10 gigabytes of shared data and costs $80 per month. Any additional data usage is billed at $15 per gigabyte. If Ms. Ruiz wants to spend at most $125 on her cell phone bill, how many additional gigabytes of data, d, could the family use?*

This situation can be represented by the inequality $80 + 15d \leq 125$.

Consider this situation:

You want your total score to be 100 points or more after your next turn in a trivia game. Each correct answer is worth 5 points. If you already have 45 points, how many more questions could you answer correctly so that your score is 100 points or more?

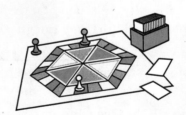

The next page shows two ways in which your child may use inequalities to determine how many more correct answers are needed.

You want your total score to be 100 points or more after your next turn in a trivia game. Each correct answer is worth 5 points. If you already have 45 points, how many more trivia questions could you answer correctly so that your score is 100 points or more?

Your child will begin to solve this problem by writing an inequality. The total number of points you want to have must be greater than or equal to 100. Let c be the number of correct answers.

Points you have   +   5 • c correct answers   must be > or =   100

45   +   5c   ≥   100

The inequality is $45 + 5c \geq 100$.

Next, solve the inequality.

$$45 + 5c \geq 100$$
$$45 - 45 + 5c \geq 100 - 45$$
$$5c \geq 55$$
$$\frac{5c}{5} \geq \frac{55}{5}$$
$$c \geq 11$$

Then, graph the solution set on a number line.

Since c is a number of questions, only whole numbers make sense. The inequality $c \geq 11$ means that the solution is any whole number greater than or equal to 11. You can graph the solution set on a number line.

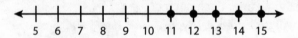

Answer: The inequality and the number line both show that the solution is any whole number greater than or equal to 11, meaning that you could answer 11, 12, 13, 14, 15, . . . questions correctly to have more than 100 points after your next turn.

Name: _____

Solve Two-Step Inequalities

Study the example showing how to solve a two-step inequality. Then solve problems 1–7.

Example

Ben sells handmade cards at a craft fair. He wants to earn more than $50 at the fair. He sells his cards for $2 and has already earned $36. How many cards does he need to sell to reach his goal?

You can write an inequality that shows the number of cards, c, that Ben needs to sell to reach his goal.	$2c + 36 > 50$
To solve, first subtract 36 from both sides of the inequality.	$2c + 36 - 36 > 50 - 36$
Simplify.	$2c > 14$
Divide both sides of the inequality by 2.	$\frac{2c}{2} > \frac{14}{2}$
Simplify.	$c > 7$

Ben needs to sell more than 7 cards to reach his goal.

1 Use this number line to show numbers in the solution set of the inequality $2s + 36 > 50$.

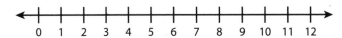

2 Do fractional solutions make sense in this context? Why or why not?

_____

3 Explain why negative integers are not in the solution set.

_____

4 Explain why Ben would not meet his goal if he sold 7 cards. How could his goal be rephrased to include 7 cards?

_____

_____

Lesson 17 Solve Problems with Inequalities   **173**

Solve.

5 Solve $2y + 12 < 42$.

Show your work.

Solution: _____

6 Manuela works as a security guard. She makes $15 per hour. Her employers deduct $125 from her weekly check to cover insurance and taxes. If Manuela receives at least $205 in her weekly paycheck, what is the fewest number of hours she works in a week? Write and solve an inequality.

Show your work.

Solution: _____

7 What non-negative integers are solutions of the inequality $|2x - 1| < 3$?

Show your work.

Solution: _____

Name: _____

The Inequality Solution

What you need: Recording Sheets, Game Board, 2 number cubes (one labeled 0–4 and "free choice and one labeled 5–9 and "free choice"), 30 markers in 2 colors

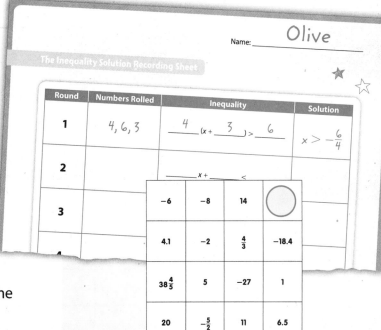

Name: _____ Olive

The Inequality Solution Recording Sheet

Round	Numbers Rolled	Inequality	Solution
1	4, 6, 3	$\dfrac{4}{}(x + 3) > 6$	$x > -\dfrac{6}{4}$
2		$\dfrac{}{}x + <$	
3			

Directions

- Your goal is to solve inequalities to mark as many Game Board squares as you can.

- Player A rolls the number cubes and records the numbers. Roll one cube again and record. If you roll "free choice," choose any number 0–9.

- Player A uses the numbers rolled to fill in the blanks to write an inequality.

- Player A solves the inequality. Player A can put a marker on one space on the Game Board that has a number within the solution set. (For example, if the solution is $x < -3$, you could put a marker on −6 or −18.4.)

- If there are no spaces on the Game Board that work, the turn ends and Player A does not place a marker.

- Players take turns. Play for 8 rounds. The player with more spaces marked wins.

Game Board:

−6	−8	14	⭕
4.1	−2	$\frac{4}{3}$	−18.4
$38\frac{4}{5}$	5	−27	1
20	$-\frac{5}{2}$	11	6.5

I think about a number line when I solve an inequality. Which part of the number line is included in the solution set? This helps me decide how to use the numbers I roll to make my inequality.

The Inequality Solution Recording Sheet

Round	Numbers Rolled	Inequality	Solution
1		_____ (x + _____) > _____	
2		_____ x + _____ < _____	
3		_____ x − _____ > _____	
4		_____ (x − _____) < _____	
5		_____ (x + _____) > _____	
6		_____ x + _____ < _____	
7		_____ x − _____ > _____	
8		_____ x − _____ < _____	

The Inequality Solution Game Board

−6	−8	14	$\dfrac{1}{2}$
4.1	−2	$\dfrac{4}{3}$	−18.4
$38\dfrac{4}{5}$	5	−27	1
20	$-\dfrac{5}{2}$	11	6.5

Name: _____

Expressions and Equations

In this unit you learned to:	Lesson
find equivalent linear expressions, for example: $1.2x + 1.3x + 0.2y + 0.1y = 2.5x + 0.3y$.	14
rewrite linear expressions in different ways, for example: $x + 0.2x = 1.2x$.	15
solve problems with equations.	16
solve problems with inequalities.	17

Use these skills to solve problems 1–7.

1 Which expression is equivalent to $4x - 5$? Select all that apply.

A $3(2x - 5) - 2(x - 5)$

B $3x - 2 - (3 - x)$

C $7x + 1 - 3(x + 2)$

D $4(2x - 1) - 2(2x - 1)$

2 Penny solved an equation by subtracting 6 from each side of the equation and then dividing each side by 5. Which of these could have been the equation Penny solved?

A $\frac{1}{5}x + 6 = 11$

B $5x - 6 = 9$

C $5x + 6 = 21$

D $6x + 5 = 17$

3 Marco sells and ships oranges from the trees in his orange grove for $1.25 per pound plus a shipping fee. One package has a shipping fee of $4.95 and a total cost of $11.20. Write and solve an equation to find the number of pounds of oranges in the package.

Show your work.

Solution: _____

Solve.

4 A store is having a sale in which the cost of any item is 35% off. Can the expression be used to find the cost, x, of an item? Select *Yes* or *No*.

a. $0.35x$ ☐ Yes ☐ No

b. $0.65x$ ☐ Yes ☐ No

c. $x + 0.35x$ ☐ Yes ☐ No

d. $x - 0.35x$ ☐ Yes ☐ No

5 Solve the inequality $4 - 3x > 16$.

Show your work.

Solution: _____

6 Barry has $30.00. He spends $9.00 for lunch. Puzzle magazines cost $4.50 each. Which graph shows how many puzzle magazines Barry could buy?

A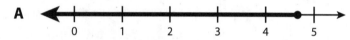

B

C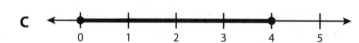

D

7 The perimeter of a rectangle is $18x + 6$. The width of the rectangle is $2x + 5$. What is an expression for the length of the rectangle?

Show your work.

Solution: _____

Name: _____

Answer the questions and show all your work on separate paper.

A local pet shelter plans to sell pet calendars to raise money for food and other supplies. Anyone can submit pictures of his or her pets, and the public will vote for their favorites to show on the calendar.

The cost to have 500 calendars printed is $2,250. Research shows that people are willing to spend between $10 and $12 for a calendar.

Find and compare the shelter's printing costs and sales earnings.

- Decide on an appropriate selling price for the calendars.
- Write an equation to find the amount of money, m, the shelter takes in for each calendar sold, c.
- Show how much money the shelter would take in by selling 50, 100, 150, 200, 250, 300, 350, 400, 450, and 500 calendars.
- Find the number of calendars the shelter would need to sell to pay for the cost of printing the calendars. Explain.

Checklist

Did you . . .

☐ select appropriate prices?

☐ write an equation?

☐ check that your answers are reasonable?

Reflect on Mathematical Practices

After you complete the task, choose one of the following questions to answer.

1 **Argue and Critique** How can you justify the selling price that you used?

2 **Model** What model did you use to show how much the pet shelter would make selling the different numbers of calendars? Why did you use this model?

Word Bank Here are some words that you might use in your answer.

equation	variable	less than
solution	greater than	compare

Models Here are some models that you might use to find the solution.

c									
m									

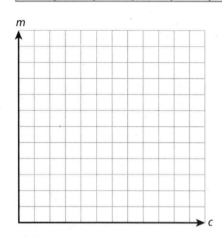

Sentence Starters Here are some sentence starters that might help you explain your work.

To decide on the selling price, _____

The shelter would need to sell _____

Name: _____

My Examples

equivalent expressions

expressions that have the same value for every value of the variable;

$2(x + 1)$ and $2 + 2x$

are equivalent expressions

distributive property

allows you to distribute a factor over the terms in a sum without changing the overall value

$2(3 + 7) = 2 \cdot 3 + 2 \cdot 7$

like terms

terms in an expression that have the same variable raised to the same power; constants are like terms

x and $-4x$

1 and 1.5

x^2 and $8x^2$

_____

_____

_____

_____

markup

a percent added to the cost of an item to determine the selling price

commission

a percent of a sales amount earned by the person making the sale

sales tax

a percent of a purchase that is added to the purchase and paid to a government

My Words

_____

_____

_____

_____

_____

_____

Dear Family,

Your child is learning about problem solving with angles.

You can use the special relationships that exist among angles to solve problems that involve angles. Some of the special relationships among angles are described below.

∠ABD and ∠DBC are complementary angles.

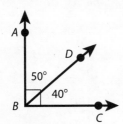

∠FGH and ∠FGI are supplementary angles.

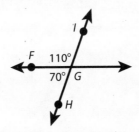

∠PQR and ∠SQT are vertical angles.

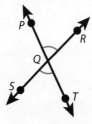

Complementary angles are angles whose measures have a sum of 90°.

Supplementary angles are angles whose measures have a sum of 180°.

Vertical angles are two non-adjacent angles formed by a pair of intersecting lines. Vertical angles have the same measure.

Consider the following example:

In the figure shown, what is the measure of ∠DCF?

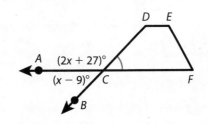

On the next page you will see two different ways your child might find the measure of ∠DCF.

In the figure shown, what is the measure of ∠*DCF*?

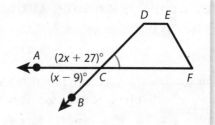

Start by finding the value of *x*. Use the diagram and facts about angles to write an equation. ∠*ACD* and ∠*ACB* are supplementary angles, so the sum of their measures is 180°.

$$(2x + 27) + (x - 9) = 180$$

Now, solve the equation to find the value of *x*.

Remove parentheses.	$2x + 27 + x - 9 = 180$
Combine like terms.	$3x + 18 = 180$
Subtract 18 from both sides.	$3x = 162$
Divide both sides by 3.	$x = 54$

Then use the value of *x* to find the measure of ∠*DCF*.

One way: ∠*ACB* and ∠*DCF* are vertical angles, so they have equal measures. Substitute 54 for *x* to find the measure of ∠*ACB*.

$$x - 9 = 54 - 9$$
$$= 45$$

The measure of ∠*ACB* is 45°, so the measure of ∠*DCF* is 45°.

Another way: ∠*ACD* and ∠*DCF* are supplemental angles, so the sum of the measures is 180°. Substitute 54 for *x* to find the measure of ∠*ACD*.

$$2x + 27 = 2(54) + 27$$
$$= 108 + 27$$
$$= 135$$

The measure of ∠*ACD* is 135°, so the measure of ∠*DCF* is $180° - 135° = 45°$.

Answer: Both methods show that the measure of ∠*DCF* is 45°.

Problem Solving with Angles

Name: _____

Study the example problem showing how to use subtraction to find unknown angle measures. Then solve problems 1–6.

Example

In most desk chairs, people sit at a 90° angle. The angle that is best for your back is 135°. What is the difference in degrees of these two sitting angles?

You can use a diagram to help you better understand the problem.

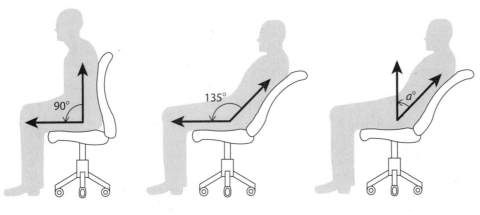

90° sitting position   135° sitting position   difference between angles

The equation 135° − 90° = *a*° represents this situation.

The difference 135° − 90° is 45°, so 45° = *a*°.

1 You can also use a protractor to help you. Start at 0° on the inside scale of the protractor. Count to 90° on the protractor. How many more degrees do you need to count to get to 135°?

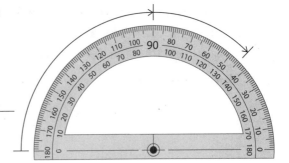

_____

2 Some desk chairs have as small as a 75° sitting position. What is the difference in degrees between sitting in this chair on its smallest setting and sitting at 135°?

Show your work.

Solution: _____

Lesson 18 Problem Solving with Angles   **191**

Solve.

3 A wheelchair ramp for a business cannot be steeper than 5°. A similar ramp for a home can be 10°. What is the difference in degrees of these two ramps? Explain.

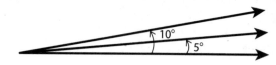

_____

4 Randi had surgery on her knee. Right after the surgery, she could bend her knee only 30° from a horizontal position. After six weeks of physical therapy, she can bend it 108°. How many more degrees can she move her knee after therapy? Explain.

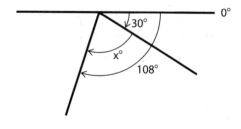

_____

_____

_____

5 Mario places a laptop on a desk. He adjusted the screen so that the screen is at an angle of 81° with the desk. What is the measure of the unknown angle? Explain.

Show your work.

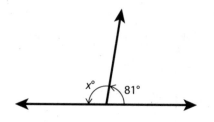

Solution: _____

6 Mansi shines a beam of light on a mirror. The angle between the beam and the mirror is 25°. The beam reflects off the mirror at an angle of 25°. Find the measure of the unknown angle.

Show your work.

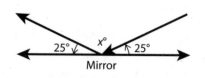

Solution: _____

Dear Family,

Your child is learning about understanding conditions for drawing triangles.

Triangles have three sides and three angles. You can try to draw a triangle with a given combination of side lengths or angle measures.

When your child is given certain conditions for the side lengths or angle measures of a triangle, he or she will find that:

- some combinations of three side lengths can form a triangle while other combinations cannot.

- triangles with the same side lengths also have the same angle measures.

- a given combination of angle measures can form many different triangles.

For example, you can't draw a triangle with side lengths of 1 inch, 2 inches, and 4 inches because two of the sides won't connect.

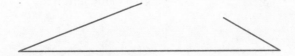

Consider these situations:

Problem A:	**Problem B:**
Draw a triangle with exactly two sides of equal length. Can you draw only one triangle or are there others?	Draw a triangle with side lengths of 3 cm and 4 cm that meet to form a 90° angle. Can you draw only one triangle or are there others?

The next page shows ways your child may solve problems involving conditions for drawing triangles.

NEXT

Problem A:
Draw a triangle with exactly two sides of equal length. Can you draw only one triangle or are there others?

Problem B:
Draw a triangle with side lengths of 3 cm and 4 cm that meet to form a 90° angle. Can you draw only one triangle or are there others?

Your child will use measurement tools such as rulers to draw sides of certain lengths and protractors to measure angles of certain measures.

Problem A:
You can draw two equal side lengths so that they meet at an acute angle. Then draw the third side length.

You can draw many other triangles by varying the angle between the two equal side lengths, so other triangles can be formed using this set of conditions.

Problem B:
You can draw a triangle with side lengths of 3 cm and 4 cm that meet to form a 90° angle. Then draw the third side length to connect the ends of the two given side lengths.

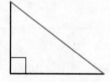

Although you can position this triangle differently by flipping it over or rotating it, it is the only one that can be drawn given this set of conditions.

Answer: Problem A shows that you can draw more than one triangle when you are given two side lengths. Problem B shows that you can draw only one triangle when you are given two side lengths and the angle measure between them.

Name: _____

Conditions for Drawing Triangles

Study the example showing conditions on the dimensions of triangles. Then solve problems 1–7.

Example

Malachi cut straws to explore which lengths could form a triangle. The table shows the pieces of straw that he cut.

Malachi's Straws

Number	2	1	2	1	1
Length (cm)	3	4	5	6	12

What three lengths could he use to make a triangle? What three lengths would fail to make a triangle?

To make a triangle, Malachi could use any three lengths that are long enough to meet. He could use two 3 cm straws and one 4 cm straw to make a triangle, while two 3 cm straws and one 6 cm straw fail to make a triangle.

Triangle:

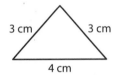

3 cm   3 cm
4 cm

Not a Triangle:

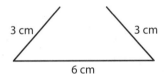

3 cm   3 cm
6 cm

1 Complete the table.

Lengths (cm) That Form Triangles	3–3–4	3–5–5		
Lengths (cm) That *Do Not* Form Triangles	3–3–6	3–5–12		

2 Explain how you completed the table.

_____

_____

_____

3 What conditions about side lengths do you think must be true in order to form a triangle?

_____

Solve.

4 Every angle in the three triangles shown measures 60°. Describe what you notice about the lengths of the sides of the triangles.

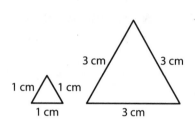 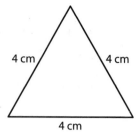

_____

_____

5 Jeremy, Luia, and Matin each drew a triangle and measured its angles. Their measurements are shown in the table.

Student	Angle Measures
Jeremy	60°–50°–70°
Luia	40°–100°–40°
Matin	20°–50°–50°

Which student must have made a mistake? How do you know?

_____

_____

6 Carrie ripped up a triangle and rearranged the corner pieces of the triangle so that the sides touch and the vertices meet at the same point. What do you notice?

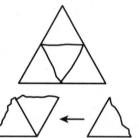

_____

7 Use the results of the problems on this page to answer the questions.

a. What condition do you think is true about the angles of a triangle?

_____

b. What is the greatest number of right angles or obtuse angles possible in a triangle? Explain.

_____

_____

Name: _____

Reason and Write

Study the example. Underline two parts that you think make it a particularly good answer and a helpful example.

Example

You are asked to create a triangle with the following conditions:

One angle of the triangle can measure no more than 25° and another angle must measure between 50° and 65°. What are the possible measures of the third angle if all angles have whole-number measures?

Explain your reasoning. Sketch and label two different triangles that justify your answer. Use the results from your work to determine the possible range of measures for the third angle in the triangle.

Show your work. Use numbers, words, and sketches to explain your answer.

For a triangle with the smallest possible angle measures of 1° and 50°, the measure of the third angle would be 180° − 1° − 50° = 129°.

For a triangle with the largest possible angle measures of 25° and 65°, the measure of the third angle would be 180° − 25° − 65° = 90°.

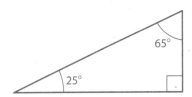

For a triangle with one angle of no more than 25° and another angle that must measure between 50° and 65°, the smallest possible third angle is 90° and the largest possible third angle is 129°. This means that the measure of the third angle, x, will be 90° ≤ x ≤ 129°.

Where does the example . . .

- explain the reasoning?

- answer all parts of the problem?

- justify with a sketch?

Solve the problem. Use what you learned from the model.

You are asked to create a triangle with the following conditions:

The noncongruent side of an isosceles triangle is 8 inches long. The perimeter of the triangle can be no more than 34 inches. What are possible measures of the congruent sides if all the side lengths are in whole inches?

Explain your reasoning. Sketch and label two different triangles that justify your answer. Use the results from your work to determine the possible range of the congruent side lengths.

Show your work. Use numbers, words, and sketches to explain your answer.

Where does the example . . .

- explain the reasoning?

- answer all parts of the problem?

- justify with a sketch?

Dear Family,

Your child is learning about area of composed figures.

Composed figures, or composite figures, are complex figures that are made up of simpler figures. Consider the following figures.

This figure is made up of rectangles.

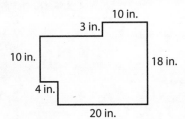

This figure is made up of a triangle and a rectangle.

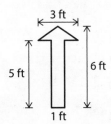

You can find the area of a composite figure by breaking the figure apart into simpler figures. You find the areas of the simpler figures and use them to find the area of the composite figure.

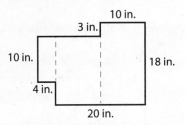

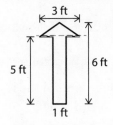

Consider the following example:

The diagram shows the dimensions of a room where the wood flooring is being replaced. How many square feet of wood flooring is needed?

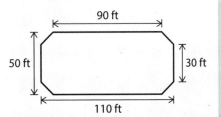

On the next page you will see two different ways your child might find the area to determine the amount of flooring needed.

A diagram shows the dimensions of a room where the wood flooring is being replaced. How many square feet of wood flooring is needed?

One way: Add to find the total area. First, separate the figure into rectangles and triangles and label the parts. Then find and add the areas of the parts.

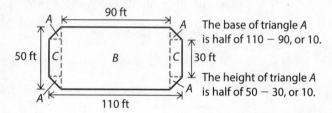

The base of triangle A is half of $110 - 90$, or 10.

The height of triangle A is half of $50 - 30$, or 10.

Find the area of each part.

Area triangle $A = \frac{1}{2}(10)(10) = 50$

Area rectangle $B = (90)(50) = 4{,}500$
Area rectangle $C = (10)(30) = 300$

There are 4 congruent triangles labeled A, 1 rectangle labeled B, and 2 congruent rectangles labeled C. Multiply and add to find the area of the floor.

$4(50) + 4{,}500 + 2(300) = 200 + 4{,}500 + 600 = 5{,}300$ square feet

Another way: Subtract to find the total area.

Draw a rectangle around the floor and find its area.
$A = \text{length} \cdot \text{width} = 110 \cdot 50 = 5{,}500$

Find the area of 1 triangle formed by the corner of the rectangle.

$A = \frac{1}{2}(10)(10) = 50$

Multiply to find the area of the 4 corner triangles: $4 \cdot 50 = 200$

Subtract: $5{,}500 - 200 = 5{,}300$ square feet

Answer: Both methods show that the area is 5,300 square feet, meaning that 5,300 square feet of wood flooring is needed.

Dear Family,

> **Your child is learning about area and circumference of a circle.**

Area is the amount of space inside a circle. Circumference is the distance around a circle.

The radius, *r*, is the distance from the center of a circle to any point on the circle. The diameter, *d*, is the distance across the center of a circle. It is twice as long as the radius.

A special relationship exists between the circumference of a circle and its diameter. The ratio of the circumference to the diameter is always the same, no matter what size the circle is.

The letter *C* stands for circumference.

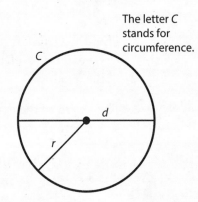

$$\frac{\text{circumference}}{\text{diameter}} = \pi \approx \frac{22}{7} \approx 3.14$$

The symbol π is pronounced "pi." The decimal 3.14 and the fraction $\frac{22}{7}$ are commonly used approximations for π. The formulas for the area and circumference of a circle involve π.

$$\text{Area: } A = \pi r^2 \qquad \text{Circumference: } C = \pi d$$

Consider this situation:

A circular stained glass window is set in a square frame. The frame is 18 inches long on each side. What is the circumference of the window? What is the area of the window?

The next page shows how your child might find the circumference and the area of the stained glass window.

A circular stained glass window is set in a square frame. The frame is 18 inches on a side. What is the circumference of the stained glass window? What is its area?

Find the circumference:
Use a diagram and a formula to find the circumference of the window.

The length of the diameter of the circle is equal to the side length of the square, 18 inches.

Use the formula for the circumference of a circle. Use 3.14 for π.

$C = \pi d$
$ = 3.14(18)$
$ = 56.52$

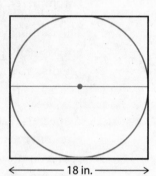

$\longleftarrow$ 18 in. $\longrightarrow$

The circumference is 56.52 inches.

Find the area:
Use a diagram and a formula to find the area of the window.

The diameter of a circle is twice as long as its radius. The diameter is 18 inches, so the radius is 9 inches.

Use the formula for the area of a circle. Use 3.14 for π.

$A = \pi r^2$
$ = 3.14(9^2)$
$ = 3.14(81)$
$ = 254.34$

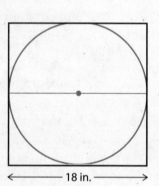

$\longleftarrow$ 18 in. $\longrightarrow$

The area is 254.34 square inches.

Answer: The circumference of the stained glass window is 56.52 inches, and the area is 254.34 square inches.

Area and Circumference of a Circle

Name: _____

Study the example showing how to find the area of a polygon. Then solve problems 1–9.

Example

A concrete company makes blocks for parking lots. A construction worker who is installing the blocks needs to find the area of the trapezoid at the end of the block.

To find the area, the worker measures the trapezoid and draws this diagram showing the measurements.

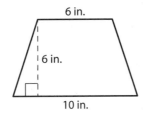

He knows how to find the area of a square and the area of a triangle. He plans to divide the trapezoid into a square and two triangles to find the area.

1 Label the dimensions in the diagram at the right.

2 Find the area of the square in the diagram.

_____

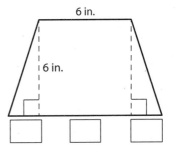

3 Find the area of one of the triangles in the diagram.

_____

4 Write and solve an equation to find the area of the trapezoid.

Show your work.

Solution: _____

Solve.

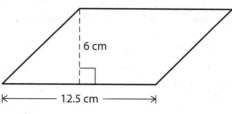

5 Use the formula for the area of a parallelogram to find the area of the parallelogram at the right.

_____

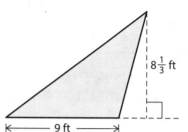

6 Use the formula for the area of a triangle to find the area of the shaded triangle at the right.

_____

7 A rectangular yard is 18 feet long. The area of the yard is 400.5 square feet. What is the width of the yard? Explain.

_____

_____

8 Divide these identical trapezoids into different sets of figures. Use these figures to find the area of each trapezoid.

Show your work.

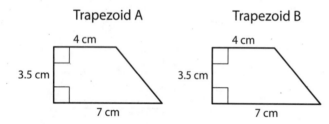

Solution: _____

9 Use the results of problem 8. Does the area of a figure depend on how it is separated into smaller figures?

_____

_____

Name: _____

Find Circumference Using a Formula

Study the example showing how to find the circumference of a circle using a formula. Then solve problems 1–9.

Example

The diameter of the outer edge of a trampoline is $14\frac{1}{2}$ feet. There is 1 foot between the outer edge of the trampoline and a safety enclosure. What is the circumference of the enclosure?

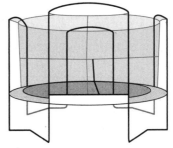

To find the circumference of the enclosure, first find its diameter. The diagram shows that the diameter of the enclosure is $14\frac{1}{2} - (2 \times 1)$, or $12\frac{1}{2}$ feet.

The formula for the circumference of a circle is $C = \pi d$, where C is the circumference and d is the diameter. Use 3.14 for π.

1 ft   1 ft

$14\frac{1}{2}$ ft

$C = \pi d = 3.14d = 3.14 \times 12\frac{1}{2} \text{ ft} = 39.25 \text{ ft}$

1 What is the circumference of the trampoline including its outer edge? Use 3.14 for π.

_____

2 What is the difference between the circumference of the trampoline and the circumference of the enclosure?

_____

3 Explain how to find the circumference of a circle if you know the radius of the circle.

_____

_____

_____

4 The United States Capitol Rotunda is a circular room located in the Capitol Building in Washington, D.C. The radius of the room is 48 feet. What is its circumference?

_____

Vocabulary

circumference the distance around a circle.

diameter the distance across a circle through the center.

radius the distance from the center to any point on a circle.

Solve. Use 3.14 for π. Show your work.

5 Pavit has a clock with a minute hand that extends to the clock's edge. The minute hand is 5.25 inches long. What is the circumference of the clock?

_____

6 The high school soccer field is decorated with the logo of the school's soccer team in a circular design. The center of the design is placed in the middle of the field. The edge of the design is $9\frac{3}{4}$ yards from its center. What is the circumference of the design?

_____

_____

_____

7 Andrea built a circular barbecue pit with a circumference of 9 feet. She wants a rod to go across the pit to use for a rotisserie. The rod must go from one edge of the pit to the other, passing through its center. To the nearest foot, how long must the rod be?

_____

_____

8 Is the relationship between the diameter of a circle and its circumference a proportional relationship? Explain why or why not.

_____

_____

9 The radius of Earth is about 6,371 kilometers and the radius of the moon is about 1,737 kilometers. Which ratio is closest to the ratio of the circumference of the moon to the circumference of Earth?

A $\frac{13}{50}$

B $\frac{21}{80}$

C $\frac{28}{101}$

D $\frac{27}{96}$

Name: _____

Find the Area of a Circle

Study the example problem showing how to find the area of a circle. Then solve problems 1–9.

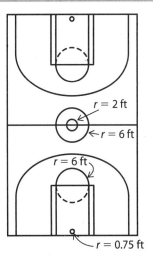

Example

Basketball courts contain several different circles. What is the area of the large center circle in the diagram? Use 3.14 for π.

The formula for the area of a circle is $A = \pi r^2$.

The radius of the large circle is 6 feet.

$A = \pi r^2 = 3.14 \times 6^2$
$= 3.14 \times 6 \times 6$
$= 3.14 \times 36 = 113.04$

The area is 113.04 square feet.

Diagram labels: $r = 2$ ft, $r = 6$ ft, $r = 6$ ft, $r = 0.75$ ft

1 What is the area of the smaller circle at the center of the court? Use 3.14 for π.

_____

_____

2 To the nearest tenth, what is the area of the circle formed by the hoop at the end of the court? Use 3.14 for π.

_____

_____

3 Describe how to find the area of a circle if you know the diameter of the circle.

_____

4 A pie is baked in a circular pan with a diameter of $10\frac{1}{2}$ inches. What is the approximate area of the pie that is left after half of the pie has been eaten?

_____

_____

_____

Solve. Use 3.14 for π.

5 Ms. Kwan's class is playing games using a circular parachute during recess. The parachute has a radius of 8 feet. What is the area of the parachute?

_____

6 Find the areas of circles with radii of 1, 2, and 4 centimeters. Then predict how the area of a circle changes when the radius is doubled.

1 cm: _____   2 cm: _____   4 cm: _____

Prediction: _____

7 How is finding the area of a circle with a given radius like finding the circumference of the circle?

_____

_____

8 The exact area of a circle is 81π square inches. What are the radius and diameter of the circle? Show your equation and explain your answers.

_____

_____

9 Simon has 18.5 feet of fencing. He makes a circular garden with the fencing. What is the area of Simon's garden to the nearest square foot?

Show your work.

Solution: _____

Name: _____

Use Areas of Circles

Study the example problem showing how to solve problems by using the areas of circles. Then solve problems 1–6.

Example

Marcella and Carlos play a game in which they drop pennies on a piece of paper to see who can cover the most area with pennies. They each have 25 pennies to drop. If a penny lands on another one, the player has to remove it and it doesn't count. A penny is about 2 centimeters in diameter.

Marcella can count 17 pennies that she dropped. To find the area Marcella's pennies cover, start by finding the area 1 penny covers.

The area 1 penny covers can be found using the formula for the area of a circle. The radius of each penny is half its diameter, or 1 centimeter.

$A = \pi r^2$

$A = 3.14 \times 1^2$

$A = 3.14 \times 1 \times 1$

$A = 3.14$ square centimeters

Multiply the area one penny covers by 17 to find the area covered by 17 pennies. So 17 pennies cover 17×3.14, or 53.38 square centimeters.

---

1 Estimate the area that would be covered by all 25 pennies.

_____

2 Use 3.14 for π to find the area that would be covered by 25 pennies. Compare your answer to your estimate in problem 1.

_____

3 Marcella and Carlos repeat the game using dimes instead of pennies. Each dime has a diameter of 0.7 inches. Carlos can count 15 dimes. To the nearest hundredth of a square inch, what area do his dimes cover on the paper?

_____

_____

Lesson 21 Area and Circumference of a Circle   **225**

Solve. Use 3.14 for π.

4 Donna bakes biscuits on a rectangular cookie sheet that is 30 centimeters by 50 centimeters. Each biscuit has a diameter of 8 centimeters.

   a. What is the maximum number of biscuits that Donna can bake at once on the cookie sheet?

   _____

   b. If Donna bakes the maximum number of biscuits, what area do the biscuits take up on the cookie sheet? Explain.

   _____

   _____

5 Find the area of the unshaded part of the figure.

Show your work.

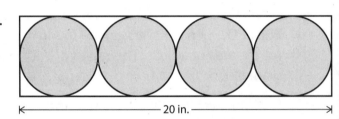

    20 in.

Solution: _____

6 A circular garden has a diameter of 6 feet. There are 2 sections of blue flowers and 1 section of white flowers as shown. What is the area of the section with the white flowers?

Show your work.

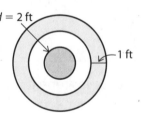

d = 2 ft

1 ft

Solution: _____

Name: _____

Area and Circumference of a Circle

Solve the problems. Use 3.14 for π.

1 The diameter of a DVD is 12 centimeters. The hole in the center of a DVD has a diameter of 1.5 centimeters.

Write and solve an equation to find the area of the DVD. Round to the nearest hundredth if necessary.

A diagram might help you solve this problem.

Show your work.

Solution: _____

2 Keb wants to put a swimming pool in his backyard. He buys a square plastic tarp to go under it. The circumference of the pool is 48 feet. The tarp is 16 feet on each side.

What is the largest pool diameter that will fit on the tarp?

a. Show that the tarp is large enough for the pool to fit entirely on the tarp.

b. To the nearest percent, what percent of the tarp will be covered by the pool?

Show your work.

Solve.

3 A gate is made up of a rectangle and a semicircle, as shown. Find the area of the gate.

Show your work.

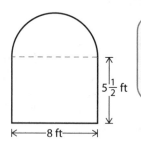

How can you find the area of a composite figure?

$5\frac{1}{2}$ ft

⟵8 ft⟶

Solution: _____

4 Tuan wants to add trim only around the edges of the gate in problem 3. How much trim does he need?

A 19.28 feet   **C** 44.12 feet

B 31.56 feet   **D** 45.56 feet

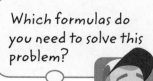

Which formulas do you need to solve this problem?

5 Chas builds a circular pen for his dog. The radius of the pen is 9.2 feet. Rounded to the nearest tenth, much fencing did Chas use for the pen?

A 28.9 feet   **C** 115.6 feet

B 57.8 feet   **D** 266 feet

Do you need to find the circumference or the area of the circle?

Skye chose **A** as the correct answer. How did she get that answer?

6 A circular plate has a radius of 12 inches. Complete the table. Include a number and a unit in the last column.

What units are used with each measure?

Property of Circle	Formula	Measure
Area		
		24 inches
Circumference		

Dear Family,

> **Your child is learning about scale drawings.**

Here are some examples of scale drawings that may be familiar to you.

- A state road map is a scale drawing of the actual roads in the state.
- A floor plan is a scale drawing of the actual layout of space in a building.
- A textbook drawing of a plant cell is a scale drawing of the actual cell.

A scale drawing shows measurements in proportion to actual measurements. You can think of a scale drawing as a reduction or an enlargement of an actual object. In the examples, the road map and floor plan are reductions. The textbook drawing is an enlargement.

Consider the following example:

An art club is planning an outdoor exhibit at a park. The scale drawing shows the design of the exhibit. A length of 1 centimeter in the scale drawing corresponds to 25 yards in the actual park. Find the dimensions of the actual park.

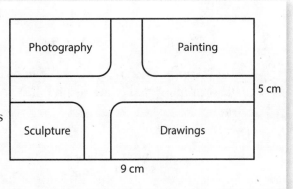

On the next page you will see two different ways your child might find the dimensions of the park.

Vocabulary

scale drawing a drawing that shows an object with its measurements in proportion to the actual measurements of the object

scale a ratio that compares the measurements used in a scale drawing with the actual measurements.

NEXT

A scale drawing is made of an art exhibit at an outdoor park. A length of 1 centimeter in the scale drawing corresponds to 25 yards in the actual park. Find the dimensions of the actual park.

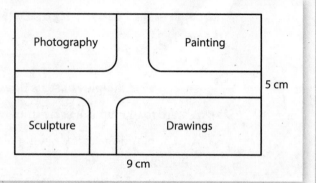

One way: Use the scale to make a table of equivalent ratios. The scale is 1 cm : 25 yd.

Distance on Scale Drawing (cm)	1	2	3	4	5	6	7	8	9
Distance in Actual Park (yd)	25	50	75	100	125	150	175	200	225

Length of scale drawing: 9 cm   Length of actual park: 225 yards
Width of scale drawing: 5 cm   Width of actual park: 125 yards

Another way: Use the scale to write equations to show the proportional relationship. Then solve each equation.

<u>Width:</u>

$$\text{drawing distance (cm)} \longrightarrow \frac{1}{25} = \frac{5}{x} \longleftarrow \text{drawing distance (cm)}$$
$$\text{actual distance (yd)} \hspace{2.5cm} \longleftarrow \text{actual distance (yd)}$$

$\frac{1}{25} = \frac{1 \times 5}{25 \times 5} = \frac{5}{125}$, so $x = 125$. The width of the park is 125 yards.

<u>Length:</u>

$$\text{drawing distance (cm)} \longrightarrow \frac{1}{25} = \frac{9}{x} \longleftarrow \text{drawing distance (cm)}$$
$$\text{actual distance (yd)} \hspace{2.5cm} \longleftarrow \text{actual distance (yd)}$$

$\frac{1}{25} = \frac{1 \times 9}{25 \times 9} = \frac{9}{225}$, so $x = 225$. The length of the park is 225 yards.

Answer: The width of the actual park is 125 yards and the length of the actual park is 225 yards.

Scale Drawings

Name: _____

Study the example problem showing how to find equivalent ratios. Then solve problems 1–8.

Example

An art teacher needs to buy 5 boxes of markers to complete a project with a class of 20 students. How many boxes of markers will he need to buy for a class of 28 students?

You can draw a diagram to represent this relationship.

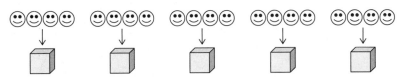

From the diagram, you can see that for every 4 students the teacher needs one box of markers.

1 Use the diagram to write a ratio that represents the number of students per box of markers. _____

2 How can you use the ratio you wrote in problem 1 to find the number of boxes of markers needed for a class of 28 students? How many boxes of markers will the teacher need to buy for a class of 28 students?

_____

_____

3 You can also use a table to relate the number of students to the boxes of markers needed. Complete the table.

Number of Students	4	20	28		40
Boxes of Markers		5		9	

4 How many boxes of markers should the teacher buy for a class of 30 students? Explain your answer.

_____

_____

Vocabulary

equivalent ratios two or more ratios that are equal to one another.

rate a comparison of the first quantity in a ratio to only one of the second quantity.

Solve.

5 Don buys 6 kiwis for $3. What would a customer pay for 9 kiwis? Explain.

_____

_____

_____

6 Aya and Jenny are playing a game in which each correct answer is worth a certain number of points. Jenny got 4 correct answers for a total of 24 points, and then it was Aya's turn. Aya scored 36 points during her turn. How many correct answers did Aya get? Explain.

_____

_____

_____

7 A school has a pep band, a sports band, a marching band, and a concert band. In each band, there are 2 trombones for every 5 trumpets. Complete the table for the bands.

Band	Trombones	Trumpets
Pep	2	
Sports	4	
Marching		20
Concert		15

8 At the Stop and Save grocery store, an 18-ounce box of Crunchy Oats costs $4.59, and a 15-ounce box costs $3.99.

a. Which box is the better buy? Explain.

_____

_____

_____

b. How much money would you save if you bought 90 ounces of cereal in the larger boxes rather than 90 ounces of cereal in the smaller boxes? Explain.

_____

_____

_____

Name: _____

Use Proportional Reasoning with Scale Drawings

Study the example showing how to use a scale drawing to find actual measurements. Then solve problems 1–7.

Example

An architect drew a scale drawing of a new art museum on centimeter grid paper. Each centimeter on the drawing represents 5 meters in the actual museum. What are the length and width of the sculpture room in the museum?

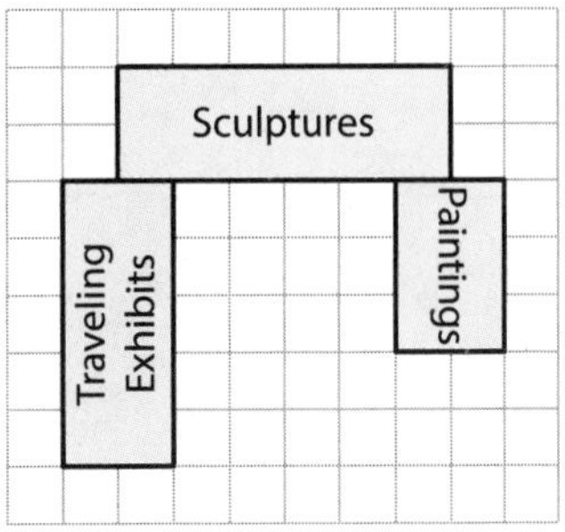

The sculpture room in the drawing is 6 centimeters long and 2 centimeters wide. The scale is 1 cm : 5 m. One way to solve the problem is to use the scale to make a table of equivalent ratios.

Distance on the Scale Drawing (cm)	1	2	3	4	5	6
Distance in the Museum (m)	5	10	15	20	25	30

The table shows, the length of the actual room is 30 meters and the width is 10 meters.

(diagram: grid showing rooms labeled "Sculptures", "Traveling Exhibits", and "Paintings")

---

1 You can also write an equation for equivalent ratios. The equation at the right can be used to find the actual length x of the sculpture room in the museum. Complete the equation and explain what each part represents.

$$\frac{1\ \text{centimeter}}{} = \frac{}{x\ \text{meters}}$$

_____

_____

_____

2 How can you use the equation to find the actual length of the sculpture room?

_____

_____

_____

Vocabulary

scale drawing a drawing that shows an object with its measurements in proportion to the actual measurements of the object.

scale a ratio that compares the measurements used in a scale drawing with the actual measurements.

3 Write and solve an equation to find the actual width of the sculpture room.

_____

Solve.

4 Trevor makes a scale drawing of a doghouse that he is building. The scale he uses is 1 in. : 0.4 ft. What is the actual area of the floor of the doghouse if the dimensions on the scale drawing are 8 in. by 10 in.?

Show your work.

Solution: _____

5 Juanita says that a scale of 1 in. : 0.4 ft is equivalent to the ratio 6 in. : 2.4 ft. Do you agree? Explain why or why not.

_____

_____

6 A car is 12.8 feet long. Jane uses a scale of 1 in. : 2 ft to make a model of the car. How long is her model?

_____

_____

7 Miko drew this scale drawing of two famous landmarks. Miko used a scale of 1 in. : 400 ft. Use equations to find the actual heights of the two structures. What is the approximate difference in their heights?

Show your work.

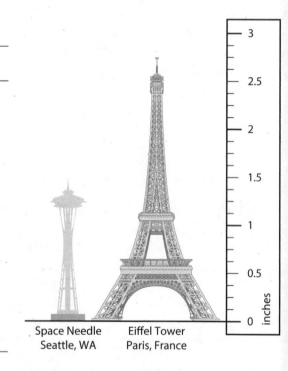

Space Needle
Seattle, WA

Eiffel Tower
Paris, France

Solution: _____

Name: _____

Redraw a Scale

Study the example showing how to redraw a scale drawing using a different scale. Then solve problems 1–9.

Example

Heather uses centimeter grid paper to draw a scale diagram of her garden. Her real garden is 32 meters by 48 meters and Heather uses a scale of 1 cm : 8 m.

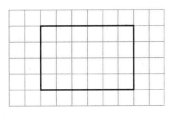

Heather needs a smaller scale drawing, so she changes the scale to 1 cm : 16 m. Now each centimeter represents 16 meters, not 8 meters.

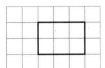

1 Calculate the dimensions of the garden using the scale 1 cm : 16 m. Are the dimensions the same as they were using the scale 1 cm : 8 m?

_____

2 How do the side lengths of Heather's new scale drawing compare to the side lengths of the original scale drawing? How can you compare the scales she used to explain this relationship?

_____

_____

3 You can also change the scale on a scale drawing to make the representation larger. Draw Heather's garden using a scale of 1 cm : 4 m.

4 Would a scale drawing of a door with a scale of 1 in. : 3 ft be longer or shorter than a scale drawing of the same door with a scale of 1 in. : 6 ft? Why?

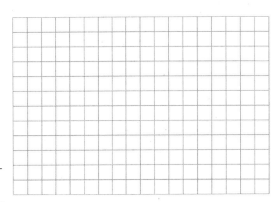

_____

_____

Solve.

5 Diagrams A and B are scale drawings of the same field. Each square is 1 centimeter long. If the scale of diagram A is 1 cm : 24 ft, what is the scale of diagram B? _____

6 What is the area of the actual field represented in problem 5? How did you find your answer?

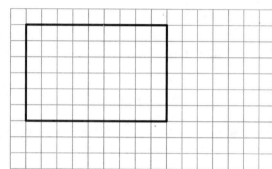

A   B

_____

_____

7 Jermaine draws a scale drawing of a porch on a grid with 1-centimeter squares. His drawing is a rectangle that is 6 cm by 9 cm, and he used the scale 1 cm : 4 ft. On this grid, redraw the scale drawing using a scale of 1 cm : 6 ft. Then find the actual area of the porch.

_____

_____

8 Anna designs model planes. Her latest scale drawing has a scale of 1 in. : 24 in. In this drawing, the wing of a plane is 4 inches long. For an advertisement, Anna has to make a larger drawing. In this drawing, the wing of the plane is 10 inches long.

a. What is the actual length of the wing in feet? Explain.

_____

b. What scale did Anna use on the advertisement drawing?

_____

9 Arty says that if you change a scale so that a unit represents a longer distance than in an original scale, then the lengths in the new scale drawing will be longer. Do you agree? Give an example of a scale and some measurements to support your answer.

_____

_____

_____

Name: _____

Scale Drawings

Solve the problems.

1 Sara uses a scale of 1 cm : 12 m to draw a floor plan of a new store. She has to redraw the drawing so that it is larger for her presentation. Could Sara use the following scales? Select *Yes* or *No* for each scale.

How long would a 12-meter wall be on each scale?

a. 1 cm : 8 m   ☐ Yes   ☐ No

b. 1 cm : 20 m   ☐ Yes   ☐ No

c. 2 cm : 24 m   ☐ Yes   ☐ No

d. 3 cm : 15 m   ☐ Yes   ☐ No

2 Gregory draws a scale drawing of his room. The scale that he uses is 1 cm : 4 ft. On this drawing, the room is 3 centimeters long. Which equation can be used to find the actual length of Gregory's room?

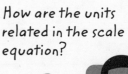

How are the units related in the scale equation?

A $\frac{1}{4} = \frac{x}{3}$ **C** $\frac{1}{4} = \frac{3}{x}$

B $\frac{x}{4} = \frac{1}{3}$ **D** $\frac{1}{x} = \frac{4}{3}$

Rob chose **A** as the correct answer. What did he do wrong?

_____

_____

3 Jon planned a bicycle ride for several of his friends. On his map, 1 inch represents 2.5 miles of actual distance. Which statements are true? Select all that apply.

Are the ratios equivalent?

A The scale of the map is 1 in. : 2.5 mi.

B A distance of 50 miles on the ride is represented by 20 inches on the map.

C Every 20 miles of the ride is represented as 2.5 inches on the map.

D A distance of 5 inches on the map represents 15 miles on the ride.

Solve.

4 The scale used to make a scale model of a volcano is 5 cm : 250 m. The height of the actual volcano is about 1,325 meters. How tall is the model?

A   26.5 cm

C   5.3 m

B   265 cm

D   26.5 m

How are equivalent ratios used to create scales?

5 Petra wants to represent a distance of 400 miles on a piece of notebook paper that is 8.5 inches wide and 11 inches long. She wants to use a scale of 1 in. = 20 mi.

a. Can Petra make this scale drawing? Why or why not?

_____

_____

_____

_____

b. Give an example of a scale that Petra could use. Use the form of 1 in. = ? mi for the scale.

_____

A model may help you solve this problem.

6 A science museum has a scale model of a ladybug. In the model, 50 centimeters represents 9 millimeters. The length of the model is 1 meter. How long is the actual ladybug?

Show your work.

Write an equation to relate the ratios.

Solution: _____

Dear Family,

Your child is learning about volume of solids.

You think of the volume of an object as the amount of space that the object occupies, or the amount of space inside the object. Here are volumes that might be important to find in certain situations.

- A farmer might need to find the volume of a farm silo.
- A gardener might need to find the volume of dirt needed to fill a raised garden bed.
- A pet owner might need to find the volume of a fish tank.

To find the volume of any object, you need to know its dimensions. You can use different formulas to find the volumes of different solid figures.

You can use the formula $V = Bh$ to find the volume of solid figures such as rectangular prisms and triangular prisms. The variable B stands for the area of the base of the solid figure and the variable h stands for the height of the solid figure.

Consider this situation:

A drawing of the doghouse Mr. Thomas built is shown. What is the volume of the doghouse?

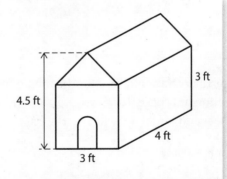

The next page shows how your child might find the volume of the doghouse.

Lesson 23 Volume of Solids   **239**

What is the volume of the doghouse?

Think about the figure as a composition of two solid figures: a triangular prism plus a rectangular prism.

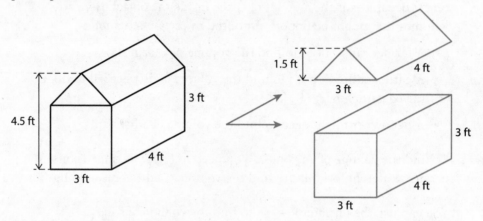

Now you can find the volumes of the triangular prism and rectangular prism.

For the triangular prism, the area of the base, *B,* is the area of its triangular base. The triangle has a height of 1.5 feet and a base length of 3 feet.

$$V = Bh$$
$$= \frac{1}{2}(3)(1.5)(4)$$
$$= 9$$

For the rectangular prism, the area of the base, *B,* is the area of its rectangular base. Here, you can use the rectangle with width of 3 feet and length of 4 feet as the base.

$$V = Bh$$
$$= (3)(4)(3)$$
$$= 36$$

Add the volumes: 9 cubic feet + 36 cubic feet = 45 cubic feet

Answer: The volume of the doghouse is 45 cubic feet.

Volume of Solids

Name: _____

Study the example showing how to find the volume of a rectangular prism. Then solve problems 1–7.

Example

Alex is constructing a box in which to grow vegetables on his patio. The box will be 6 feet long, 2 feet wide, and $3\frac{1}{2}$ feet deep. What is the volume of soil needed to fill the box?

You can model the volume using 1-foot unit cubes. Notice that the first three layers are whole cubes, and the top layer is made up of half-cubes.

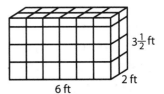

Cubes in one of the bottom 3 layers: $6 \cdot 2 = 12$

Total cubes in the bottom 3 layers: $3 \cdot 12 = 36$

Cubes in the top layer: $\frac{1}{2}(6 \cdot 2) = 6$

Total cubes needed to fill the box: $36 + 6 = 42$

Alex needs 42 cubic feet of soil to fill the box.

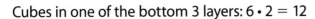

1 Why do you multiply 12 by 3 to find the total number of cubes in the bottom 3 layers?

_____

2 Why do you multiply $(6 \cdot 2)$ by $\frac{1}{2}$ to find the number of cubes in the top layer?

_____

_____

_____

3 Use the formula $V = lwh$ to find the volume of the box. Compare the volume found using the formula with the volume computed above.

_____

Solve.

4 A rectangular box of pasta is 10 inches long, 8 inches wide, and $2\frac{1}{4}$ inches deep. What is the volume of the box?

_____

5 Meghan says that the formula $V = Bh$, where B is the area of the base, can be used to find the volume of any rectangular prism. Do you agree? Explain.

_____

_____

6 Lao is thinking of buying a fish tank. Tank A has a base area of 530 square centimeters. Which fish tank has the greater volume? How much greater?

Show your work.

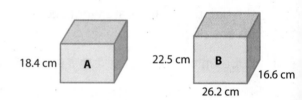

18.4 cm   A   22.5 cm   B   16.6 cm   26.2 cm

Solution: _____

7 If you double the length, the width, and the height of a rectangular prism, how does the volume of the prism change? Use algebra to justify your answer. Then give a numerical example.

Show your work.

Solution: _____

Name: _____

Volume of Prisms

Study the example problem showing how to find the volume of a prism. Then solve problems 1–7.

Example

A triangular prism is shown at the right. What is the volume of the prism?

The bases of this prism are the right triangles at either end of the prism. So, first find the area of one of the bases.

$\frac{1}{2}bh = \frac{1}{2}(6)(8) = 24$

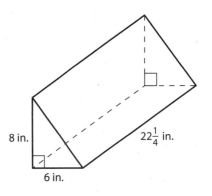

8 in.

6 in.

$22\frac{1}{4}$ in.

The area of a triangular base is 24 square inches.

Next, use the formula $V = Bh$, where B is 24 and h is $22\frac{1}{4}$.

$V = Bh = 24(22\frac{1}{4}) = 534$

The volume of the prism is 534 cubic inches.

---

1 How do you know that the right triangles are the bases of the prism?

_____

2 Describe the faces of the prism that are not bases. How are they alike? How are they different?

_____

_____

3 A second prism has dimensions that are $\frac{1}{2}$ of the dimensions of the prism in the example. Kathy says that the volume of the smaller prism is $\frac{1}{2}$ of the volume of the prism in the example. Do you agree? Explain.

Show your work.

Solution: _____

Solve.

4 What is the volume of the prism shown?

Show your work.

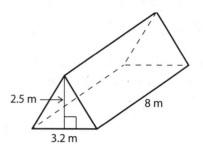

2.5 m 8 m 3.2 m

Solution: _____

5 A pentagonal prism is shown. The volume of the prism is 91.8 cubic inches. If the height of the prism is 10.8 inches, what is the area of each base? Explain.

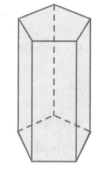

_____

_____

6 A store sells two types of tiny crystals. One of the crystals is a triangular prism whose dimensions are shown at the right. The other crystal is shaped like a rectangular prism with a length of 26 millimeters, a width of 8.5 millimeters, and a height of 7 millimeters. Alice says that the volume of the rectangular crystal is greater than two times the volume of the triangular crystal. Find the volumes to prove whether or not Alice is correct.

Show your work.

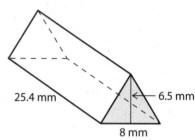

25.4 mm 6.5 mm 8 mm

Solution: _____

7 Use the diagram at the right to write a formula in terms of *b*, *h*, and *l* for the volume of a triangular prism.

Show your work.

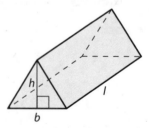

h *l* *b*

Solution: _____

Name: _____

Volume of Complex Solids

Study the example showing how to find the volume of a composite solid. Then solve problems 1–7.

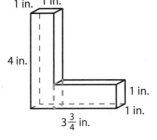

Example

Lázaro is designing a set of blocks for young children. He needs to know the volume of the block shown.

First he draws lines to divide the block into two rectangular prisms. Then he draws the two prisms and labels the dimensions of each.

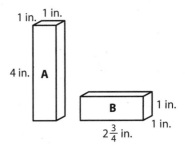

Volume of prism A = $1 \times 1 \times 4 = 4$

Volume of prism B = $2\frac{3}{4} \times 1 \times 1 = 2\frac{3}{4}$

Total volume of block = $4 + 2\frac{3}{4} = 6\frac{3}{4}$

The block has a volume of $6\frac{3}{4}$ cubic inches.

---

1 How did Lázaro find the length of prism B?

_____

_____

2 Draw lines to show two other ways that Lázaro could divide the block into other prisms.

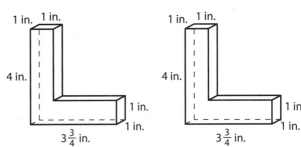

3 Choose one of the ways in which you divided the block in problem 2. Sketch the prisms, label the dimensions of each one, and find the total volume.

Show your work.

Solution: _____

Solve.

4 How is the process for finding the volume of a complex three-dimensional figure like the process for finding the area of a complex two-dimensional figure?

_____

_____

Use the figure at the right for problems 5–7.

5 Sierra is designing a stage platform with a ramp. Draw lines on the figure at the right to divide the figure into solid figures whose volume you know how to find.

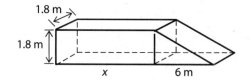

6 The total volume of the stage and ramp is 42.12 square cubic meters. Find the width of the stage, *x*.

Show your work.

Solution: _____

7 Sierra decides to add a set of stairs to the stage on the side opposite the ramp. Each stair has the same width and height. By how much does the volume of the structure increase?

Show your work.

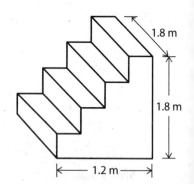

Solution: _____

©Curriculum Associates, LLC   Copying is not permitted.

Name: _____

Volume of Solids

Solve the problems.

---

1 What is the volume of the figure shown?

Show your work.

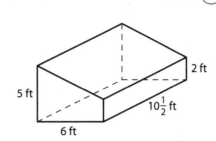

What shapes make up this solid?

Solution: _____

---

2 How do the volumes of the two figures compare? Select all that are correct.

A Volume A = Volume B

B Volume A = $\frac{1}{2}$ Volume B

C Volume A > Volume B

D Volume B > Volume A

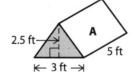

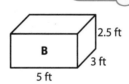

How can you answer without actually computing the volumes?

---

3 Jayden needs to store boxes that are 4 feet long, 3 feet wide, and 2 feet high. The boxes must remain upright with one of the 4-foot by 3-foot sides on top. Jayden's storage locker is 12 feet long, 6 feet wide, and 9 feet high. What is the greatest number of boxes that he can store in the locker?

Be sure to satisfy all conditions of the problem.

A 24   **B** 27   **C** 30   **D** 32

June chose **B** as her answer. How did she get that answer?

_____

_____

Solve.

4 Find the volume of each figure. Tell whether each statement is *True* or *False*.

A: 3 cm, 3 cm, 6.5 cm

B: 2 cm, 2 cm, 6 cm, 2 cm, 2 cm, 11.5 cm

C: 3 cm, 3 cm, 13 cm

Do you have to compute the volumes of figures A and C to know if they are the same?

a. Figure B has the greatest volume. ☐ True ☐ False

b. Figures A, B, and C have equal volumes. ☐ True ☐ False

c. No two figures have equal volumes. ☐ True ☐ False

d. Only figures A and B have equal volumes. ☐ True ☐ False

5 A child's toy is made by removing a triangular prism from the center of a wooden rectangular prism. The triangular base of the triangular prism has a base length of 1 inch and a height of 1 inch. Write and solve an equation to find the volume of the toy.

$3\frac{1}{2}$ in. $3\frac{1}{2}$ in.   8 in.

Should you add or subtract to find the volume?

Show your work.

Solution: _____

Dear Family,

> **Your child is learning about the surface area of solids.**

Here are some examples of situations that involve surface area.

- A house painter finds the surface area of the exterior of a house to determine how much paint is needed.

- A factory needs to order enough cardboard to make into boxes.

- A store manager keeps a sufficient amount of wrapping paper in stock for wrapping gift boxes.

To find the surface area of a solid figure, you can find and add the areas of all of its faces. For example, a box can be thought of as a rectangular prism. Rectangular prisms have six rectangular faces. You can find the area of each rectangular face by using the formula for the area of a rectangle. Then you add the areas of all of the faces to find the surface area of the box.

You can find the surface area of a solid figure with triangular and rectangular faces, such as the triangular prism shown below, in a similar manner. Use the formula for the area of a triangle as well as the formula for the area of a rectangle.

Consider the following example:

A museum exhibit of modern art includes a glass triangular prism with the dimensions shown at the right. How many square feet of glass were needed to make the prism?

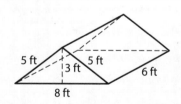

On the next page you will see two different ways your child might find the surface area of the glass triangular prism.

NEXT

A museum displays a glass triangular prism with the dimensions shown. How many square feet of glass were needed to make the prism?

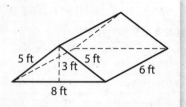

You can draw and label the dimensions of the five faces of the prism. The bases are two congruent triangles. The other faces are three rectangles, two of which are congruent.

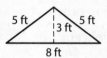 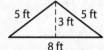

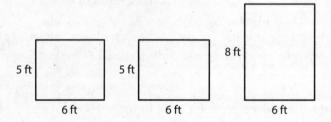

Use formulas to find the areas of the faces.

Area of a triangle:

$A = \frac{1}{2}bh = \frac{1}{2}(8)(3) = 12$

Area of the 5-foot by 6-foot rectangle:
$A = lw = (6)(5) = 30$

Area of the 8-foot by 6-foot rectangle:
$A = lw = (8)(6) = 48$

One way: Add all five areas.
12 + 12 + 30 + 30 + 48 = 132

Another way: Use multiplication and then add.
2(12) + 2(30) + 48 = 132

Answer: Both methods show that the surface area of the triangular prism is 132 square feet, so it took 132 square feet of glass to make the prism.

Surface Area of Solids

Name: _____

Study the example showing how to use a net to find the surface area of a prism. Then solve problems 1–7.

Example

Kioshi needs to find the surface area of a triangular prism with the dimensions shown. He begins by drawing a net of the triangular prism and labeling the dimensions of each face. Find the area of each face of the prism.

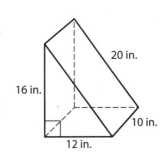

You can make a table that shows the dimensions and the area of each face of the prism.

Face	Base (in.)	Height (in.)	Area (sq in.)
Triangle	12	16	96
Triangle	12	16	96
Rectangle	10	12	120
Rectangle	10	16	160
Rectangle	10	20	200

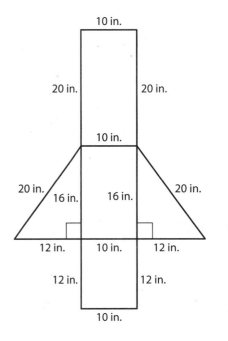

1. Why do the two triangles have the same base length and height? How did you find the area of each triangle?

_____

_____

2. Do all the rectangles have equal areas? Explain.

_____

_____

_____

3. What is the surface area of the prism? Explain how you found the surface area.

_____

Vocabulary

net a flat representation of a solid when it is "unfolded."

surface area the sum of the areas of all of the faces of a three-dimensional figure.

Solve.

4 A doorstop is a triangular prism with the dimensions shown. Label the side lengths (in centimeters) of the net for the doorstop.

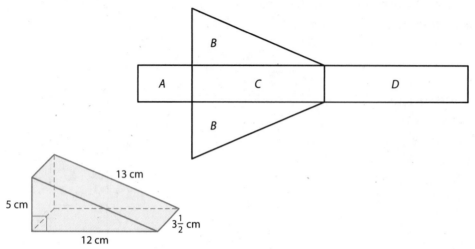

5 Using the letters in each section of the net in problem 4, write and solve an equation to find the total surface area of the prism, S.

_____

_____

6 Write an expression that represents the surface area of any rectangular prism with length l, width w, and height h. Explain.

_____

_____

7 The height of a rectangular prism is 20 centimeters. It has a surface area of 2,400 square centimeters. What are two possible sets of lengths and widths? Find one set of dimensions with l and w equal in length as well as a set of dimensions that are not equal.

Show your work.

Solution: _____

Name: _____

Surface Area of a Triangular Prism

Study the example problem showing how to find the surface area of a triangular prism. Then solve problems 1–7.

Example

The bases of the prism shown are isosceles triangles. What is the surface area of the prism?

You can draw the faces of the prism, label the dimensions, and find the area of each face. There are two identical triangular faces. Draw and label one of them and find its area.

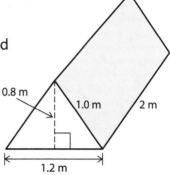

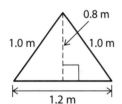

$A = \frac{1}{2}(1.2)(0.8) = 0.48$

Draw and label one of the identical rectangular faces. Then draw the third rectangular face. Find the areas.

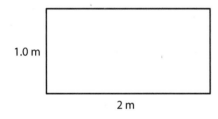

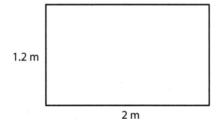

$A = (1.0)(2) = 2$ $A = (1.2)(2) = 2.4$

Surface area $= 2(0.48) + 2(2) + 2.4 = 7.36$ square meters

---

1 What formula was used to find the area of the triangular faces?

_____

2 What formula was used to find the area of the rectangular faces?

_____

3 Why is the area of one of the rectangles different from the areas of the other two rectangles?

_____

Solve.

4 A manufacturer packages a product in a box shaped like a triangular prism with a height of 5.0 centimeters. The dimensions of the bases of the prism are shown. Draw each rectangular face of the box. Label the dimensions. Write the area of each rectangle inside it.

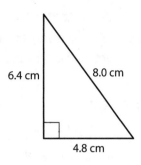

6.4 cm

8.0 cm

4.8 cm

5 Write and solve an equation to find the surface area of the prism in problem 4.

Show your work.

Solution: _____

6 If the height of the box in problem 4 is doubled from 5 centimeters to 10 centimeters, does the surface area double? Explain your result.

Show your work.

Solution: _____

7 Find an expression for the surface area of a cube with edges of length *s*. Justify your answer.

_____

_____

©Curriculum Associates, LLC   Copying is not permitted.

Name: _____

Surface Area of a Complex Solid

Study the example showing how to find the surface area of a complex solid. Then solve problems 1–5.

Example

Tiana has a storage box with the dimensions shown. To find the surface area, she draws and labels the faces of the prism as shown. Make a table with the area of each face.

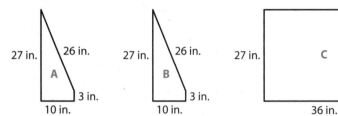
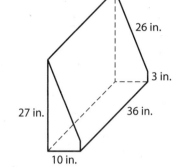
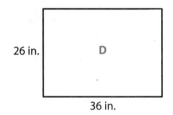
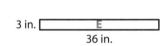

You can use the formulas you know to find the area of each figure that Tiana drew. Notice that figures A and B are composed of a triangle and a rectangle.

Face	Area (sq in.)
A	$A = (3)(10) + \frac{1}{2}(10)(24) = 150$
B	$A = (3)(10) + \frac{1}{2}(10)(24) = 150$
C	$A = (36)(27) = 972$

Face	Area (sq in.)
D	$A = (36)(26) = 936$
E	$A = (36)(3) = 108$
F	$A = (36)(10) = 360$

1 What is the surface area of the box?

_____

2 Chris says that he can find the surface area faster by thinking of the box as a triangular prism on top of a rectangular prism. He finds the surface area of each one and adds them together. Does his method make sense?

_____

_____

Solve.

3 Milo is making a set of blocks for his child-care business. He has a block that is a triangular prism. He cuts the top off of this block to make a smaller triangular prism, which he paints red. A diagram of the original triangular face is shown. What is the surface area that Milo paints red?

Original Block

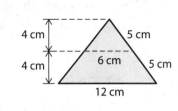

Show your work.

Solution: _____

4 Refer to problem 3. Milo paints the lower piece green. Draw one of the trapezoidal faces and label its dimensions. What is the surface area of the block that Milo paints green?

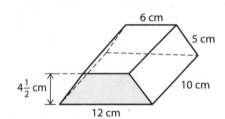

Show your work.

Solution: _____

5 A metal machine part is 21 millimeters long, 21 millimeters wide, and 4 millimeters thick. A square that is 6 millimeters on each side is punched from the middle of the metal solid. What is the surface area of the resulting figure?

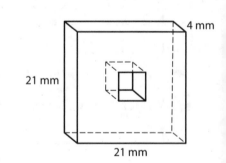

Show your work.

Solution: _____

Name: _____

Surface Area of Solids

Solve the problems.

1 Viola says that she can find the surface area of a rectangular prism by finding the area of one face and multiplying by 6. When is this true? When is this *not* true? Use diagrams to explain your answer.

Think about the dimensions of a rectangular prism.

Show your work.

Solution: _____

_____

2 Which expression can be used to find the surface area of the triangular prism represented by the net? Select all that apply.

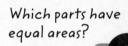

Which parts have equal areas?

A $3(10 \cdot 5) + 2\left(\frac{1}{2}\right)(6 \cdot 4)$

B $2(10 \cdot 5) + (10 \cdot 6) + 2\left(\frac{1}{2}\right)(6 \cdot 4)$

C $(18 \cdot 16) - 4(5 \cdot 4) - 4\left(\frac{1}{2}\right)(3 \cdot 4)$

D $(18 \cdot 16) - 2(5 \cdot 4) - 2\left(\frac{1}{2}\right)(3 \cdot 4)$

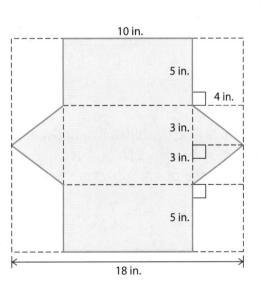

Solve.

3 What is the surface area of the prism shown?

A 1.5 square meters

B 1.8 square meters

C 2.16 square meters

D 2.4 square meters

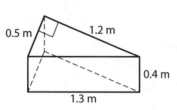

How many faces does this prism have?

4 A storage box without a top is $18\frac{1}{4}$ inches long, 15 inches wide, and 10 inches high. The outside of the box is painted yellow. What is the total area that is painted yellow? Explain.

Would drawing a diagram help?

_____

5 Lyle sliced a block of cheese along a diagonal into two triangular prisms, as shown. Lyle says that the surface area of the block is 2 times the surface area of one of the triangular prisms. Do you agree? Explain your answer.

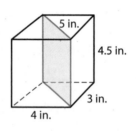

How can you compare the surface areas?

_____

_____

_____

_____

6 Refer to problem 5. Find the difference between the surface area of the two triangular prisms and the surface area of the rectangular prism. Show your work.

What operation does the word difference indicate?

_____

_____

_____

_____

Dear Family,

Your child is learning about plane sections of prisms and pyramids.

A plane section of a solid figure formed by making a straight cut through the figure is called a cross-section. You can think of a cross-section as the two-dimensional shape formed when you slice through a figure.

Cross-sections can be many different shapes and sizes. It all depends on how a figure is sliced. The vertical slice through the rectangular prism at the right results in a rectangular cross-section.

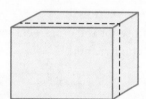
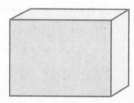

However, a slanted slice through the corner of the same prism results in a triangular cross-section.

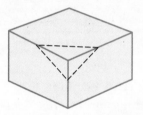
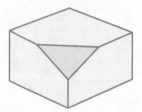

Consider this situation:

How could you slice the square pyramid shown to get a square for the cross-section? How could you slice it to get a triangle for the cross-section?

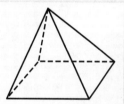

The next page shows how your child may get cross-sections of the pyramid that are a square and a triangle.

Vocabulary

cross-section a two-dimensional shape formed by making a straight cut through a section of a three-dimensional figure.

Lesson 25 *Understand* Plane Sections of Prisms and Pyramids   **259**

NEXT

How could you slice the square pyramid shown to get a square for the cross-section? How could you slice it to get a triangle for the cross-section?

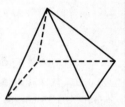

Square cross-section:

To get a square for the cross-section, make a horizontal slice parallel to the base of the pyramid.

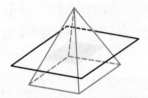

Triangular cross-section:

To get a triangle for the cross-section, make a vertical slice from the top of the pyramid to its base that is perpendicular to the base.

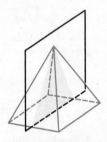

Answer: A square pyramid can be sliced parallel to its base (horizontally) to get a square for the cross-section, and it can be sliced perpendicular to its base from the top of the pyramid (vertically) to get a triangle for the cross-section.

Understand
Plane Sections of Prisms and Pyramids

Name: _____

> **Prerequisite: How do you identify shapes according to their properties?**

Study the example showing how to identify shapes by using their properties. Then solve problems 1–8.

Example

The Venn diagram at the right shows the relationship between plane figures, polygons, triangles, quadrilaterals, and pentagons.

The most general category is plane figures, which include any closed two-dimensional shapes. This category includes polygons because polygons are closed plane figures with straight sides. Polygons include figures such as triangles, quadrilaterals, and pentagons because each of these figures is a closed plane figure with straight sides.

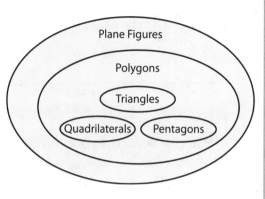

1. Fill in the blanks using the categories in the Venn diagram.

   Quadrilaterals are both _____ and _____.

2. An oval is a plane figure.

   a. Is an oval a polygon? Explain your answer.

   _____

   b. Does an oval belong in the Venn diagram hierarchy shown above? Explain.

   _____

   _____

   _____

3. Where would you include rectangles in the Venn diagram?

   _____

   _____

Vocabulary

hierarchy a ranking of categories based on properties.

Solve.

4 The flowchart at the right shows the relationship between polygons, quadrilaterals, and squares, ordered from general to specific from top to bottom. Mike makes a similar flowchart that shows the relationship between quadrilaterals, rectangles, and parallelograms, ordered from general to specific from top to bottom. Fill in the types of shapes to show the correct order.

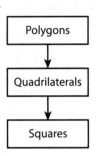

Top: _____ Middle: _____ Bottom: _____

5 Refer to the flowchart in problem 4. Name a property of squares that is not a property of all quadrilaterals.

_____

_____

Use the Venn diagram for problems 6–7.

6 Fill in the boxes to complete the Venn diagram.

7 Fill in the blanks below.

The Venn diagram shows that rectangles,

_____, and rhombuses are all

_____. Also, _____

are both rectangles and rhombuses.

Rhombuses   Rectangles

8 Draw a Venn diagram that includes the following: quadrilaterals, rhombuses, parallelograms, rectangles, and squares. Explain how you drew your diagram.

_____

_____

_____

_____

_____

_____

Name: _____

Cross-Sections of Three-Dimensional Figures

Study the example problem showing how to visualize cross-sections of three-dimensional figures. Then solve problems 1–8.

Example

Juaquin is baking cookies using cookie batter formed in the shape of a cylinder. How could he cut the cylinder to make circular cookies?

Cutting a cross-section parallel to the circular bases produces a circle.

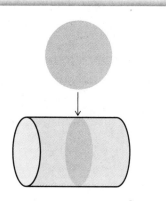

1 Suppose Juaquin wants to make rectangular cookies. How could he cut the cylinder to form rectangles from the dough?

_____

_____

2 Juaquin reshapes the dough into another three-dimensional shape that could have a circular cross-section. What is one shape Juaquin could have made?

_____

3 When you cut a cross-section of a three-dimensional shape, how many dimensions is the cross-section? Explain.

_____

_____

4 A cross-section taken of the cube shown is a triangle. Describe how the cube could have been sliced to produce that cross-section.

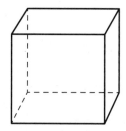

_____

_____

_____

Solve.

Use the information below and the diagram to solve problems 5–6.

A concrete block like the one shown is often used as a support for construction posts. The top and base of the block are squares.

5 What shape results from a horizontal cross-section of the concrete block? Name and sketch the shape of this cross-section.

6 What shape results from a vertical cross-section of the concrete block? Name and sketch the shape of this cross-section.

7 Connie cut several cross-sections from a solid rubber ball.

  a. How would the cross-sections be alike?

  _____

  b. How would the cross-sections be different?

  _____

8 Ken says that he can produce four different plane figures from slicing a square pyramid. Is Ken correct? If so, name the figures and describe the slices that produce them. If not, explain why not.

_____

_____

_____

_____

_____

Name: _____

Reason and Write

Study the example. Underline two parts that you think make it a particularly good answer and a helpful example.

Example

Consider making the same slice through the figures below.

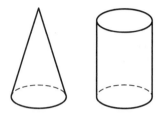

Describe the slices that would produce the following cross-sections.

- cross-sections that are the same shape

- cross-sections that are different shapes

Name and draw each cross-section produced by the slices.

Show your work. Use words and diagrams to explain your answer.

If I slice the two figures parallel to their bases, the cross-sections will both be circles.

If I slice the two figures through their centers and perpendicular to their bases, the cross-sections will be different. The cross-section of the cone will be a triangle. The cross-section of the cylinder will be a rectangle.

Where does the example . . .

- *answer each part of the problem?*
- *use both words and diagrams?*
- *provide details?*

Solve the problem. Use what you learned from the model.

The same slice was made through two different three-dimensional figures. The cross-section shown below was produced from both figures.

A second slice was made through the figures in a different way than the first slice. The cross-sections shown below were produced from each figure.

Name and sketch the two solids that could be sliced to produce the cross-sections above. Describe how they were sliced to produce the given cross-sections.

Show your work. Use words and diagrams to explain your answer.

Did you . . .

• answer each part of the problem?

• use both words and diagrams?

• provide details?

Shape Up

What you need: Recording Sheets, number cube 2–7,
Shape Up Cards

Directions

- Your goal is to score points by finding
  the area, circumference, surface area, or
  volume of a given figure.

- Mix the cards and place them in a pile
  facedown. Player A picks a card. The
  player keeps the card if there is an empty space on
  the Recording Sheet that matches it. If there are
  no empty spaces for that figure, player A puts the
  card on the bottom of the pile and skips a turn.

- Player A rolls the number cube as many times as
  needed to get dimensions for the shape. Record
  the dimensions on the Recording Sheet and find
  the measurement listed there.

- Both players check the work. If correct, Player A
  scores 1 point. If incorrect, mark 1st Try and score
  0. Player A may try to complete this space later,
  after picking the card again.

- Players take turns. The first player to get 6 points
  wins. If players use up their tries before anyone
  gets 6 points, the player with the most points
  wins.

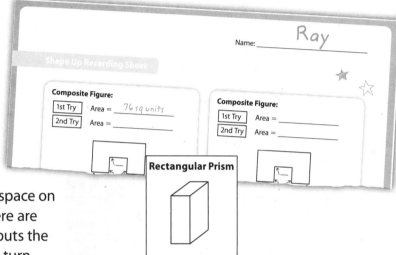

> I remember that
> volume is the space
> inside a solid figure.
> And surface area is
> just what it says, the
> area of the surface
> of the figure. That
> means I add the
> areas of each face
> of the figure.

Shape Up Recording Sheet

Composite Figure:

| 1st Try | Area = _____ |
| 2nd Try | Area = _____ |

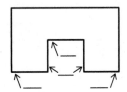

Score: _____

Composite Figure:

| 1st Try | Area = _____ |
| 2nd Try | Area = _____ |

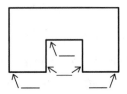

Score: _____

Rectangular Prism:

| 1st Try | Surface Area = _____ |
| 2nd Try | Surface Area = _____ |

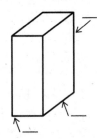

Score: _____

Rectangular Prism:

| 1st Try | Volume = _____ |
| 2nd Try | Volume = _____ |

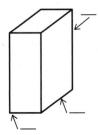

Score: _____

Circle: (Use 3.14 for π.)

| 1st Try | Area = _____ |
| 2nd Try | Area = _____ |

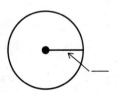

Score: _____

Circle: (Use 3.14 for π.)

| 1st Try | Circumference = _____ |
| 2nd Try | Circumference = _____ |

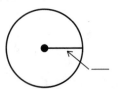

Score: _____

Shape Up Game Cards

Circle	Rectangular Prism	2-Dimensional Composite Figure
	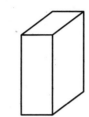	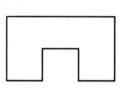
Circle	**Rectangular Prism**	**2-Dimensional Composite Figure**
	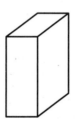	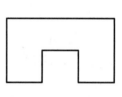
Circle	**Rectangular Prism**	**2-Dimensional Composite Figure**
	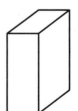	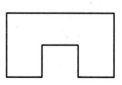

Geometry

In this unit you learned to:	Lesson
solve problems with angles.	18
draw triangles to meet given conditions.	19
find the area of composed figures and circles.	20, 21
solve problems with scale drawings.	22
find the surface area and volume of solid figures.	23, 24
describe plane sections of prisms and pyramids.	25

Use these skills to solve problems 1–6.

1 The measure of $\angle ABC$ is 40°.

Part A: What is the measure of the supplement of $\angle ABC$?

_____

_____

Part B: What is the measure of the complement of $\angle ABC$?

_____

_____

2 What is the ratio of the area of the circle to the area of the quadrilateral? Write your answer in terms of π.

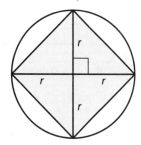

_____

3 Kamilah has a cone. She slices it in several different ways. Which of these *cannot* be the shape of one of the cross-sections?

  A circle

  B triangle

  C oval

  D rectangle

4 From which measures can a triangle be drawn? Select all that apply.

  A angles 40°, 40°, and 100°

  B angles 50°, 75°, and 95°

  C sides 4 cm, 4 cm, 10 cm

  D sides 6 cm, 8 cm, 10 cm

Solve.

5 A construction company uses a model of a concrete block in the design of a building. The model is shown, and its scale is 1 inch = 2 feet.

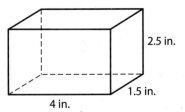

2.5 in.

1.5 in.

4 in.

Part A: What are the actual dimensions of the concrete block?

_____

Part B: What is the surface area of one concrete block in square feet?

_____

Part C: Fifty of the concrete blocks are needed for the building. What is the volume of the concrete needed to make 50 blocks?

_____

_____

6 Mark wants to paint the wall shown below.

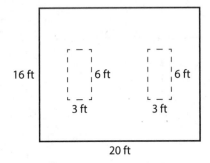

16 ft

6 ft   6 ft

3 ft   3 ft

20 ft

The wall has two windows. What is the area of the wall that can be painted?

Show your work.

Solution: _____

©Curriculum Associates, LLC   Copying is not permitted.

Answer the questions and show all your work on separate paper.

Two of the attractions at Springdale Pride Day will take place in the field at the park. There needs to be a pathway that is 20 feet wide to separate the two attractions. In this scale drawing of the field, 1 inch = 100 feet.

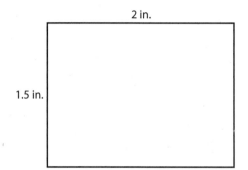

2 in.

1.5 in.

Here are sketches of the two attractions with some dimensions given.

Choose a length between 60 and 80 feet for the straight sides of the corral and a length that is at least 100 feet for the softball throw that will work with all requirements.

Find the actual dimensions of the field and area of each composite shape, showing all your work.
(Use 3.14 for π.) Justify that both shapes will fit on the field and can be separated by a 20-foot walkway. You may want to draw and label a diagram.

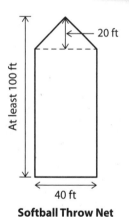

20 ft

60–80 ft

20 ft

Pony Ride Corral

20 ft

At least 100 ft

40 ft

Softball Throw Net

Reflect on Mathematical Practices

After you complete the task, choose one of the following questions to answer.

1 **Model** Did you make a drawing to find your solution? How did it help?

2 **Argue and Critique** In addition to the given information, what other factors did you consider when deciding what lengths to use?

Word Bank Here are some words that you might use in your answer.

scale	width	rectangle
length	area	triangle
		circle

Model Here is a model that you might use to find the solution.

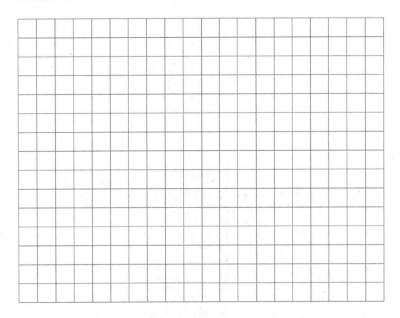

Sentence Starters Here are some sentence starters that might help you explain your work.

I can break the corral shape into _____

To find the area _____

Unit 4 Vocabulary

My Examples

supplementary angles

two angles whose measures add up to 180°

vertical angles

congruent angles formed when two lines intersect

complementary angles

two angles whose measures add up to 90°

polygon

a closed plane figure whose sides are line segments that intersect only at their endpoints

circumference

the distance around a circle

diameter

the distance across a circle through the center

radius

the distance from the center of a circle to any point on the circle

equivalent ratios

two or more ratios that are equal to one another

rate

a comparison of the first quantity in a ratio
to only one of the second quantity

scale drawing

a drawing that shows an object with its
measurements in proportion to the actual
measurements of the object

scale

a ratio that compares the measurements
used in a scale drawing with the actual
measurements

net

a flat representation of a solid when it is
"unfolded"

surface area

the sum of the areas of all of the faces of a three-dimensional figure

hierarchy

a ranking of categories based on properties

My Words

Dear Family,

> **Your child is learning about random samples.**

When you want to gather information about an entire group, or population, it is often hard to survey each member of the group. It is more practical to survey a sample of the group. You want a sample that is representative of the population, or else your sample will be biased.

- In a biased sample, certain people are more likely to be chosen than others, making the sample a bad representation of a population.

- In a random sample, each person has an equal chance of being chosen, making it a good representation of a population.

When you use a random sample to conduct a survey, you can use the data that you collect to make generalizations about the entire population. However, if you use a biased sample, any generalizations that you make will be inaccurate.

Suppose you want to find which supermarket people in your town prefer. You can survey a sample of people to predict the preference of the entire town.

- You get a biased sample if you ask people who are exiting a particular supermarket.

- You get a random sample if you use a list of town residents and ask every fifth person on the list.

Consider the following example:

A dance school director wants to know what type of dance the students at her school like best. Describe a random sample that the director could use to gather this information and explain why it is a good sample. Then describe a biased sample and explain why it is biased.

On the next page you will see two samples your child might use to describe a random sample and a biased sample.

A dance school director wants to know what type of dance the students at her school like best. Describe a random sample that the director could use to gather this information and explain why it is a good sample. Then describe a biased sample and explain why it is biased.

Random sample:
Determine a method to create a random sample.

- Write the names of all current dance students on slips of paper.

- Place all of the slips of paper in a large bowl.

- Mix the slips all around and choose one slip.

- Repeat until you have reached the number of students that you want to survey.

- Ask the students whose names you chose to name their favorite type of dance.

This is a random sample of students because each student has an equal chance of being chosen.

Biased sample:
Determine a method to create a biased sample.

- Ask all students exiting the ballet class what their favorite type of dance is.

This is a biased sample because it includes only students who are enrolled in ballet class. It is more likely that they will choose ballet over other types of dance. All students do not have an equal chance of being chosen using this sampling method.

Answer: The first method shows that creating a random sample means making sure that each person in the population has an equal chance of being included in the sample. The second method shows that a biased sample is created when each person in the population does not have an equal chance of being included in the sample.

Understand
Random Samples

Name: _____

Prerequisite: **What are statistical questions?**

Study the example showing the difference between a statistical question and a non-statistical question. Then solve problems 1–6.

Example

Statistical question:

You ask the students in your class: "What is your height?"

When you ask a statistical question, you expect to get a variety of answers. The answers have variability. The question above is statistical because you expect to get different answers.

Non-statistical question:

You ask the students in your class: "What is the height of the tallest student in the seventh grade?"

When you ask a non-statistical question, there is only one correct answer and you expect the same answer from everyone you ask.

---

1 You ask the students in your class two questions. Which question is statistical and which is non-statistical? Explain.

• What time does the first period begin?

• What time do you leave home to go to school?

_____

_____

_____

_____

Vocabulary

statistical question a question that is expected to have variability in the data related to it.

variability the extent to which data are different from each other.

2 Write both a statistical question and a non-statistical question you could ask some classmates to gather information about playing video games.

_____

_____

_____

Solve.

3 Silvie asked students in the cafeteria: "How many miles do you live from school?" Determine whether Silvie's question is *statistical* or *non-statistical*. Explain your answer.

_____

_____

4 If you ask your classmates, "How many problems were on the math quiz?", you are not asking a statistical question. What is a statistical question you might ask about the quiz? Explain.

_____

_____

_____

5 Look at problem 4. Explain why the non-statistical question does not have variability.

_____

_____

6 Evan surveyed his classmates to make a prediction about seventh-grade students. Look at his results in the table.

Hours	3	4	5	6	7
Number of Students	2	4	6	5	3

Write two statistical questions that Evan could have asked to get his results. Then explain why Evan could not have asked a non-statistical question to get his results.

_____

_____

_____

_____

Name: _____

Identify Random and Biased Samples

Study the example problem showing how to tell whether a sample is a random sample or a biased sample. Then solve problems 1–7.

Example

The school cafeteria manager wants to survey students about their favorite lunch item. Do you think Survey Method 1 creates a random sample or a biased sample? Explain.

Since only females will be surveyed, this method does not give everyone in the population an equal chance of being chosen. The method creates a biased sample.

Survey Method 1: Survey 50 female students in the cafeteria at lunch.

---

1 Write *random* or *biased* for the type of sample that each survey method will create.

Survey Method 2: Survey 50 students whose names are chosen without looking from a box containing all students' names.

Survey Method 3: Survey 50 students who are on the football and soccer teams.

_____   _____

2 Describe a different survey method the manager could use that will create a random sample.

_____

_____

3 The manager decides to survey 100 students instead of 50. If the sample is random, which sample size is more likely to represent the population? Explain.

_____

_____

_____

_____

Vocabulary

random sample
a sample in which every element in the population has an equal chance of being selected.

biased sample a sample that does not represent the whole population.

population the entire group considered for a survey.

Solve.

4 You want to find out which music store in town is the most popular. Which survey method is more likely to create a representative random sample? Explain.

- You survey customers coming out of Best Sounds music store.

- You survey people at several different shopping areas in town.

_____

_____

_____

5 Mr. Lee wants to survey 20 of the 210 students in the seventh grade about the hours they sleep each night. He finds that 2 of the 20 students surveyed sleep for 9 hours each night. About how many of the 210 seventh graders sleep for 9 hours each night? Explain how you found your answer.

_____

_____

_____

6 You want to know the favorite band of the 25 students in your math class. Should you survey the whole class, which is the entire population, or a sample of students from the class? Explain.

_____

_____

7 Koby visits one randomly selected science class from each grade and surveys the first ten students who leave the room. What question could he ask so that this group is a random sample? What question could he ask so that this group is a biased sample? Explain.

_____

_____

_____

_____

Name: _____

Reason and Write

Study the example. Underline two parts that you think make it a particularly good answer and a helpful example.

Example

Select a topic and a population from the lists below for a survey.

Topic	Population
Favorite store at the local mall	Teachers in your school
Favorite snack	Students in your school
Time to get to work or school	Shoppers at the local mall

Describe the attributes of the people that should be represented in a random sample of your population.

Then describe a sample for this population that could be considered biased. Explain why it might be biased.

Show your work. Use words to explain your answer.

Possible answer: I chose *favorite store at the local mall* as my topic and *shoppers at the local mall* as my population.

A random sample should represent people with different opinions and interests. It should also include people from different groups, such as males, females, adults, and children. I would want a random sample to have an equal number males and females from different age groups.

A sample that includes only shoppers in one age group at a specific store would be a biased sample. For example, surveying only teenagers coming out of a clothing store or surveying only children coming out of a toy store would produce a biased sample. The sample does not represent all shoppers in the mall and the method does not give all the shoppers an equal chance of being selected.

Where does the example . . .

- answer each part of the problem?
- give details or examples?
- explain the reasoning?
- use math vocabulary?

Solve the problem. Use what you learned from the model.

Select a topic and a population from the lists below for a survey.

Topic	Population
Favorite color	Students in your school
Favorite sports team	Students in your grade
Number of pets	Store customers

Describe the attributes of the people that should be represented in a random sample of your population. Then describe how you would create a random sample of the population to participate in the survey. Explain how you know that the sample is representative of the population.

Show your work. Use words to explain your answer.

Did you . . .

• answer each part of the problem?

• give details or examples?

• explain the reasoning?

• use math vocabulary?

Dear Family,

Your child is learning about making statistical inferences.

Your child has already learned about random samples. Now your child is learning how to understand the results of random samples.

One random sample may differ from another random sample, even when the same population is used. This is called random variation. For example, suppose you have a bag of 100 marbles, some of which are black and the rest are white. You take 10 marbles from the bag, note their colors, and return them to the bag. Then you repeat this process.

• The first sample may have 2 white marbles and 8 black marbles.

• The second sample may have 4 white marbles and 6 black marbles.

The data from multiple samples helps you make estimates about the number of black marbles and white marbles in the bag. The more samples you have, the better prediction you can make.

Consider this situation:

A box contains 100 buttons. Some are red, and the rest are pink. A random sample of 10 buttons is drawn, and the number of red buttons is noted. The 10 buttons are returned to the box. The process is repeated to get a total of 15 random samples. The table shows the results.

Sample Number	1	2	3	4	5	6	7	8	9	10	11	12	13	14	15
Number of Reds	8	7	8	3	7	5	10	7	7	4	6	8	9	8	7
Proportion of Reds	0.8	0.7	0.8	0.3	0.7	0.5	1.0	0.7	0.7	0.4	0.6	0.8	0.9	0.8	0.7

What is a good estimate for the number of red buttons in the box?

The next page shows two ways your child may organize the data from the random samples in order to make a prediction.

A box contains 100 buttons. Some are red, and the rest are pink. A random sample of 10 buttons is drawn, and the number of red buttons is noted. The 10 buttons are returned to the box. A total of 15 samples are drawn. The table shows the results.

	1	2	3	4	5	6	7	8	9	10	11	12	13	14	15
Number of Reds	8	7	8	3	7	5	10	7	7	4	6	8	9	8	7
Proportion of Reds	0.8	0.7	0.8	0.3	0.7	0.5	1.0	0.7	0.7	0.4	0.6	0.8	0.9	0.8	0.7

What is a good estimate for the number of red buttons in the box?

One way: Use a dot plot.

The dot plot shows that the proportion of reds in many of the samples was either 0.7 or 0.8, but there are more samples at 0.7.

There are 100 total buttons in the bag, so the number of red buttons in the bag is probably closer to 0.7(100) = 70 than 0.8(100) = 80. A good estimate is around 70 red buttons.

Buttons Experiment

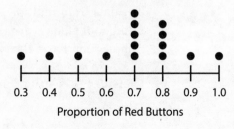

Proportion of Red Buttons

Another way: Use a box plot.

The box plot shows that the median of the proportions is 0.7.

There are 100 total buttons in the bag, so the number of red buttons in the bag is probably around 0.7(100) = 70.

Buttons Experiment

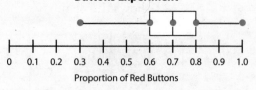

Proportion of Red Buttons

Answer: Both methods show that the average proportion of red buttons in the 15 samples is near 0.7, so a good estimate for the number of red buttons in the box is around 70.

Making Statistical Inferences

Name: _____

**Study the example showing random and biased samples.
Then solve problems 1–6.**

Example

The students in Mr. Walker's class want to find out about the favorite rainy day activities of their middle school's entire student population.

Random Sample:

Brielle surveyed one randomly chosen student from each of the 20 homerooms in the school.

Brielle's sample is random because every student in the school had an equal chance of being selected.

Biased Sample:

Asa surveyed 20 randomly chosen members of the school's book club.

Asa's sample is biased because all the students she surveyed are part of one group, the book club.

---

1 To find the information described in the example, Pam surveyed the 23 students in her Grade 7 math class. Is her sample *random* or *biased*? _____

2 To find the information described in the example, Nick surveyed every 15th student who entered the school building. Is his sample *random* or *biased*? _____

3 Pam asked for volunteers to take her survey about rainy day activities. Why might a sample created by asking for volunteers be biased?

_____

_____

_____

_____

_____

_____

Vocabulary

random sample a sample in which every element in the population has an equal chance of being selected.

biased sample a sample that does not represent the whole population.

Lesson 27 Making Statistical Inferences   **289**

Solve.

4 Vivek plans to survey 10 randomly chosen residents out of the 280 people that live in his community about plans for a new neighborhood dog park. Describe one way he can make the sample more likely to represent the population of residents.

_____

_____

5 Three park rangers had to report about the ways visitors use their facilities. Each ranger surveyed a sample of park visitors. Compare the methods. Do you think all three rangers' samples are equally representative of their parks' visitors? Explain.

- Ranger Li surveyed 30 randomly chosen visitors to her park's information center.

- Ranger Simpson divided his park into 30 same-sized zones and surveyed one randomly chosen visitor encountered in each zone.

- Ranger Patel surveyed 30 randomly chosen people who posted reviews of the park on a fishing website.

_____

_____

_____

_____

6 Jackson uses a random number generator to choose 20 students from each grade and asks how long they spend on homework. Niko says that Jackson's sample is biased. Do you agree? Explain. If it is biased, identify a different 60-student sample that can be chosen to better represent the school population.

Jackson's School

Grade	Students
6	300
7	150
8	150

_____

_____

_____

_____

Name: _____

Represent Distributions of Statistics

Study the example showing how to represent distributions of statistics from random samples. Then solve problems 1–6.

Example

A box contains 80 loose white or yellow golf balls. Each student in Mr. Koger's class drew a random sample of 20 balls from the box, counted the yellow balls, and then returned the sample to the box.

Nate calculated the proportion of balls in each sample that were yellow, and then he organized the results in the following table.

Student	1	2	3	4	5	6	7	8	9	10	11	12
Number of Yellows	6	5	6	8	5	7	3	6	2	6	6	5
Proportion of Yellow	0.3	0.25	0.3	0.4	0.25	0.35	0.15	0.3	0.1	0.3	0.3	0.25

1 Marta believes it will be easier to identify clusters of data if the results are represented with a dot plot. Do you agree? Explain.

_____

2 Create a dot plot to display the proportion of yellow balls in each sample.

3 According to the data, what is a good estimate for the number yellow balls in the box? Explain.

_____

_____

Solve. Use the following situation for problems 4–6.

A box in Ms. Booth's class contains 200 loose white or yellow golf balls. The table below represents the results when 11 students each drew a random sample of the same number of balls, counted the number of yellows, and then returned the sample to the box.

Student	1	2	3	4	5	6	7	8	9	10	11
Proportion of Yellow	0.6	0.7	0.3	0.7	0.5	0.9	0.8	0.8	0.7	0.7	0.9

4 Which graphic representation of the data (a table, a dot plot, or a box plot) would best help estimate the number of yellow balls in the box?

_____

_____

_____

5 Construct a box plot to display the data from Ms. Booth's class.

6 Lana believes a good estimate of the number of yellow balls in the box is 70 balls. Do you agree? Explain how she may have arrived at that answer.

_____

_____

_____

_____

Name: _____

Compare Samples of Different Sizes

Study the example showing how to compare the distributions of the results from samples of different sizes. Then solve problems 1–7.

Example

Louise and Aiden are experimenting with a bag of 90 pink or brown marbles. Louise drew 5 marbles, calculated the proportion that were brown, and returned the marbles. She drew 12 samples. Aiden conducted the same steps but used samples of 10 marbles. Their results are represented by the stacked dot plots at the right.

Notice that the same number line is used in both plots. This makes it easier to compare the spread and clustering of the data.

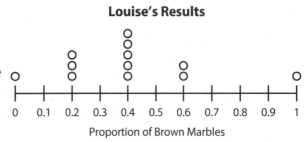

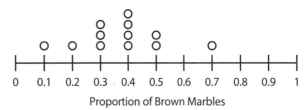

1. Compare the shapes of the two distributions from Louise and Aiden's experiments.

_____

2. Compare the centers of the two distributions from Louise and Aiden's experiments.

_____

3. Compare the spreads. Which distribution is more spread out?

_____

4. If Jo repeats the experiment but draws 20 marbles in each sample, how would you expect a dot plot of her results to compare to Louise and Aiden's plots? Explain your reasoning.

_____

_____

_____

Lesson 27 Making Statistical Inferences   **293**

Solve.

Ken and Seyi experimented with a bag containing 250 red, white, or black marbles. They each drew a sample of marbles from the bag, calculated the proportion of the sample that was white, and returned the marbles to the bag. They repeated these steps 15 times, and created the box plots at the right to represent the results of their experiments.

Ken's Results

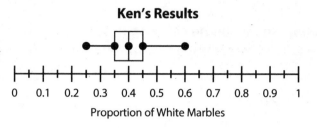

Proportion of White Marbles

5 Each of Seyi's samples contained 20 marbles. Do you think Ken used a larger or smaller sample size in his experiment? Explain your reasoning.

Seyi's Results

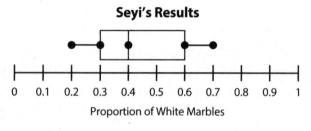

Proportion of White Marbles

_____

_____

6 If you could only use one sample to make a prediction about the number of white marbles in the bag, would you rather use one of Ken's samples or one of Seyi's samples? Why?

_____

_____

_____

7 The dot plot shown represents the data from Seyi's experiment. Suppose Haley used the same bag of 250 marbles and repeated Seyi's experiment 15 times using 10 marbles as her sample size. Create a dot plot on the number line underneath Seyi's plot to show a realistic set of data from Haley's experiment.

Seyi's Results

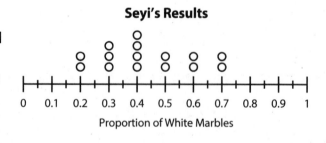

Proportion of White Marbles

Haley's Results

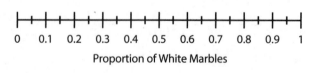

Proportion of White Marbles

Name: _____

Making Statistical Inferences

Solve the problems.

1 Gianna wanted to estimate the mean number of words per page in the 180-page book she is reading. Which of these sampling methods gives the best estimate of the mean word count per page in the book?

What makes a sample biased?

A Count the words on one randomly chosen page.

B Calculate the mean word count for a sample consisting of the 30 pages with photographs.

C Calculate the mean word count for a sample of 20 pages selected by choosing every 9th page.

D Calculate the mean word count for a sample consisting of the 10 pages that appear to have the most words.

2 A representative sample of 80 customers in a clothing store was surveyed about how they paid for their purchases. The table shows the responses.

How can you write the data in the table as proportions?

Payment Method	Number of Customers
Cash	20
Check	12
Credit Card	24
Debit Card	16
Gift Card	8

Based on the survey results, choose *True* or *False* for each statement.

a. Tomorrow, 8 out of the first 80 customers will pay with a gift card. ☐ True ☐ False

b. In a group of 40 customers, it is expected that about 10 will pay with cash. ☐ True ☐ False

c. About 0.3 of all the store's customers will pay with a credit card. ☐ True ☐ False

d. A sample of 100 customers would provide less reliable results. ☐ True ☐ False

Solve.

3 Suppose you spun the fair spinner shown 10 times and recorded the number of times you landed on "Blue." Then 8 of your friends did the same thing. Without actually using a spinner, make a dot plot to show a realistic set of data for this situation. Your plot's number line should show the proportion of blue in each person's sample.

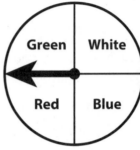

Green | White

Red | Blue

4 Suppose you and your friends decided to redo the experiment in Problem 3 using the same spinner but making 40 spins each. Explain how a dot plot representing this new data compares to the original.

_____

_____

_____

5 Val asked a random sample of 50 students at her school if they brought lunch from home today. If 30 answered "yes," about what percent of students at Val's school brought lunch from home today?

A 15%   **C** 50%

B 30%   **D** 60%

Trey chose **B** as the correct answer. How did he get that answer?

_____

_____

_____

Dear Family,

> **Your child is learning about using mean and mean absolute deviation to compare data.**

You can compare two sets of data by looking at the centers and variability of each data set and at the way the data in each set is distributed. Comparing two sets of data allows you to see whether there is overlap in the data sets.

One way to look at the center of data is to find the mean, or average. One way to look at the variability of data is to find the mean absolute deviation (MAD), or the average distance that the data values are away from the mean.

By comparing the means and the MADs of two sets of data, you can tell whether the sets of data are likely to have no overlap, some overlap, or a lot of overlap. Knowing how data is distributed can help with making decisions based on the data.

Consider the following example:

A fitness company has a chain of fitness clubs. The company wants to compare the lengths of members' visits at clubs in two different locations. The dot plots below show the data for a sample of 10 members at each club. Use the mean and MAD for each data set to compare the data sets.

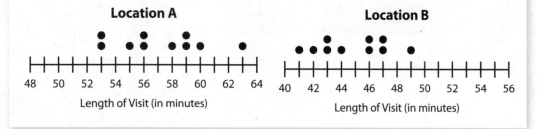

On the next page you will see how your child might use the mean and the mean absolute deviation for each data set to compare them.

Find the mean and MAD for each data set and compare them. What can you tell about the lengths of the visits at the two clubs?

Find the mean for each data set:

Find the means by adding the data values and dividing by the number of values.

The mean length of a visit at Location A is 57.2 minutes.

The mean length of a visit at Location B is 44.8 minutes.

Find the MAD for each data set:

Find the differences from the mean. The mean of the absolute values of those differences is the MAD.

Location A:

Length of Visit	53	53	55	56	56	58	59	59	60	63
Difference from Mean	4.2	4.2	2.2	1.2	1.2	−0.8	−1.8	−1.8	−2.8	−5.8

MAD:

$$\frac{4.2 + 4.2 + 2.2 + 1.2 + 1.2 + 0.8 + 1.8 + 1.8 + 2.8 + 5.8}{10} = 2.6$$

Location B:

Length of Visit	41	42	43	43	44	46	46	47	47	49
Difference from Mean	3.8	2.8	1.8	1.8	0.8	−1.2	−1.2	−2.2	−2.2	−4.2

MAD:

$$\frac{3.8 + 2.8 + 1.8 + 1.8 + 0.8 + 1.2 + 1.2 + 2.2 + 2.2 + 4.2}{10} = 2.2$$

Answer: The means tells that the average length of a visit is 57.2 minutes at Location A and 44.8 minutes at Location B. The MADs are about the same, 2.6 and 2.2. This indicates that the variability is similar in both sets of data. The difference between the means (57.2 − 44.8) is 12.4, which is about 5 times the MADs, so there is virtually no overlap between the data sets.

Using Mean and Mean Absolute Deviation to Compare Data

Name: _____

Study the example showing how to describe the center of a data set using mean, median, and mode. Then solve problems 1–6.

Example

Miguel keeps track of his number of hits in baseball games this year. His data set is:

{3, 2, 5, 3, 0, 2, 3, 5, 4}

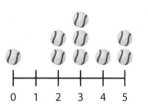

He draws a dot plot to represent these data. How can Miguel describe the center of the data set?

One way that Miguel can describe the center of the data set is by finding the *mean,* or average, of the data. To find the mean, add the numbers together and divide by the total number of values.

Sum = 0 + 2 + 2 + 3 + 3 + 3 + 4 + 5 + 5 = 27

Mean = $\frac{27}{9}$ = 3

Miguel's average is 3 hits per game.

1 What is the median of Miguel's data? Show how you found your answer.

_____

_____

2 How can you use a dot plot to identify the mode of a data set?

_____

_____

_____

3 What is the mode of Miguel's data?

_____

_____

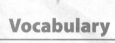

Vocabulary

mean the average of a data set.

median the middle number in an ordered set of numbers.

mode the most common number in a set of numbers.

Lesson 28 Using Mean and Mean Absolute Deviation to Compare Data   **299**

Solve.

4 Janna's health class measures the heart rates of students after they walked for five minutes. The heart rates, in beats per minute, were {102, 74, 86, 74, 96, 95, 103, 102}. Find the mean of the data set. What does the mean tell you?

Show your work.

Solution: _____

_____

5 Bayo measured the distance in inches that a toy car traveled after going down a ramp. She collected this data for seven trials: {117, 135, 117, 139, 121, 133, 22}.

a. An *outlier* is one or more data values that are quite different from the other data values in the set. Are there any outliers in Bayo's data? If so, which one(s)? _____

b. Which measure of center (mean, median, or mode) is most affected by an outlier? Justify your answer.

_____

_____

c. What measure of center would you use to describe this data set? Explain.

_____

_____

6 Kobe collected data on the weight, in pounds, of 5 different dogs at an animal shelter. The mean of his data was 38, the median was 37, and the mode was 35. Give an example of a data set with these measures of center. Show that your data set meets the requirements.

Name: _____

Comparing Variabilities and Centers

Study the example showing how to compare data sets that have similar variabilities. Then solve problems 1–9.

Example

Mr. Markum is ordering sneakers for the boys' baseball team. The sizes ordered and the number of pairs of each size are shown in the table. To the nearest tenth, the mean size of the sneakers for the baseball team is 10.6. What is the mean absolute deviation (MAD)?

Sneaker Size	8.5	9	9.5	10	10.5	11	11.5	12
Number	1	2	0	2	3	4	1	3
Difference from Mean Size	2.1	1.6	0	0.6	0.1	−0.4	−0.9	−1.4

To find the MAD of the sneaker sizes, subtract each data value from the mean. Then average the absolute values of these numbers and round to the nearest tenth.

$$\frac{2.1 + (2 \times 1.6) + (2 \times 0.6) + (3 \times 0.1) + (4 \times 0.4) + 0.9 + (3 \times 1.4)}{16} = \frac{13.5}{16} \approx 0.8$$

1 Mr. Markum also orders sneakers for the girls' softball team. He makes the table below. The mean size of the sneakers to the nearest tenth is 8.2. Complete the table.

Sneaker Size	7	7.5	8	8.5	9	9.5	10
Number	2	3	5	1	3	1	1
Difference from Mean Size							

2 Calculate the MAD of the softball sneaker sizes to the nearest tenth.

_____

3 What is the difference in the mean sizes of the two types of sneakers? What is the difference in their MADs? Interpret the differences in the means and MADs.

_____

_____

_____

Solve.

The table gives average speeds of eight horses in a horse race and eight cars in a car race. Use the table to solve problems 4–9.

Number	1	2	3	4	5	6	7	8
Speed of Horse (mph)	29	30	27	25	27	26	27	23
Speed of Car (mph)	233	228	229	234	231	228	232	226

4　Calculate the mean of the horses' speeds to the nearest tenth. Then calculate the mean of the cars' speeds to the nearest tenth.

5　Calculate the MAD of the horses' speeds to the nearest tenth. Calculate the MAD of the cars' speeds to the nearest tenth.

6　Were the horses' speeds or the cars' speeds closer to their mean? Explain.

_____

_____

7　What is the difference in the means? _____

8　By what number would you have to multiply the MAD of the cars' speeds to get the difference between the means that you found in problem 7? Round your answer to the nearest tenth.

_____

9　What do your answers to problems 4, 5, and 8 tell you about the two data sets? Your answers should refer to the means and the MADs of the data sets.

_____

_____

_____

Name: _____

Using Mean and Mean Absolute Deviation to Compare Data

Solve the problems.

1 Which of the following measures the variability of a data set?

A MAD   **C** median

B mean   **D** mode

Brandon chose **B** as the correct answer. How did he get that answer?

_____

_____

> What is the definition of each term?

2 Tell whether each statement is *True* or *False* for the following data set: {5, 7, 12, 3, 7, 8}.

a. The mean is 8. ☐ True ☐ False

b. The data set has no mode. ☐ True ☐ False

c. A deviation of 3 from the mean is −4. ☐ True ☐ False

d. The MAD is 2. ☐ True ☐ False

> How do you compute the mean, mode, and MAD?

3 Which of the following results show similar variability but noticeably different centers? Select all that apply.

A Data set 1: Mean = 2.4; MAD = 26.9
Data set 2: Mean = 2.2; MAD = 25.3

B Data set 1: Mean = 6.7; MAD = 33.2
Data set 2: Mean = 2.0; MAD = 35.0

C Data set 1: Mean = 1.1; MAD = 32.8
Data set 2: Mean = 1.0; MAD = 5.1

D Data set 1: Mean = 10.3; MAD = 2.2
Data set 2: Mean = 37.2; MAD = 2.4

> What measure indicates the variability of a data set?

Solve.

4 Which of the following is *not* true about the mean of a set of data?

A   The mean can be one of the data values.

B   The mean can be different from all of the data values.

C   The mean can be less than the minimum data value.

D   The mean can be the same value as the median.

Try constructing data sets with the given characteristics.

5 Gerald kept track of the high temperatures for two weeks, and he recorded the results in a table.

Day	Sunday	Monday	Tuesday	Wednesday	Thursday	Friday	Saturday
Week 1 Temp. (°F)	52	65	63	48	52	53	60
Week 2 Temp. (°F)	59	62	63	60	56	55	54

a.   Calculate the difference between the weekly mean high temperatures rounded to the nearest tenth.

_____

How do you calculate the mean of a data set?

b.   Compare and interpret the MADs of weeks 1 and 2.

_____

_____

_____

6 Create two sets of data with the following characteristics:

•   Each data set has 5 values.

•   The mean of set 1 is greater than the mean of set 2.

•   The MAD of set 1 is less than the MAD of set 2.

_____

_____

_____

_____

Use examples of data sets that you have seen to help you solve this problem.

Dear Family,

Your child is learning about using measures of center and variability to compare data.

You can compare two data sets by using measures of center and variability. Measures of center describe the middle of a set of data. One measure of center may better represent a data set than another.

- *Mean* is the average of the numbers in the data. *Median* is the middle number in the data. *Mode* is the most common number in the data.

Measures of variability describe how the data varies.

- *Range* is the difference between the greatest and least numbers in the data set. *Mean absolute deviation* is the average distance that the data values are away from the mean. *Interquartile range* describes the middle 50% of the data.

Dot plots and box plots help you visualize data sets to better compare them.

Consider this situation:

A consumer agency tests tires so that shoppers can compare brands. The graphs show the results of the testing. Use the statistical graphs to compare the results.

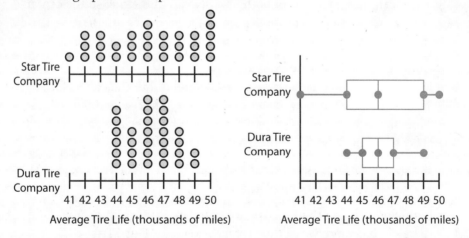

The next page shows how your child might use measures of center and variability to compare the data sets.

Lesson 29 Using Measures of Center and Variability to Compare Data   **305**

Use the statistical graphs to compare the data sets.

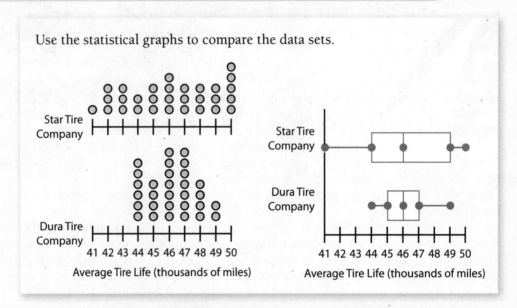

Comparing measures of center:

Dot plot: The median of both data sets is 46. The mode of Star Tire is 50, and the modes of Dura Tire are 46 and 47. The means are both 46.2.

Box plot: You can only tell the median from a box plot. The median of both sets is 46.

The means and medians of both data sets are the same, so the centers of data are the same. The modes are not a good measure here because the mode for Star Tire is not representative of a typical value.

Comparing measures of variability:

Dot plot: The shape of both data sets is similar, but the values for Star Tire are more spread out. The range is 9 for Star Tire and 5 for Dura Tire. The MAD for Star Tire will be greater because the data are farther away from the mean than the data for Dura Tire.

Box plot: The range is 9 for Star Tire and 5 for Dura Tire. The IQR is 5 for Star Tire and 2 for Dura Tire.

Both plots tell you that the data for Star Tire is more spread out, and therefore has more variability, than the data for Dura Tire.

Answer: The measures of center for the data sets are very close, except for the mode. Dura Tires data has less variability so their tires are likely to be a more consistent product.

Using Measures of Center and Variability to Compare Data

Name: _____

Prerequisite: Shape of Data Points on a Graph

Study the example showing how to describe the shape of a graph. Then solve problems 1–7.

Example

Twelve students in each of three different seventh-grade classes sell flowers to raise money for a class trip. The line plots for each class are shown. Each student is represented by one X. Describe the shape of the graph for Ms. Marcum's class.

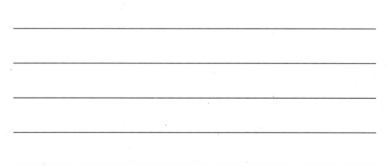

The graph for Ms. Marcum's class is *symmetrical* because the same number of data points fall above and below the *peak* at 4.

1 Describe the shapes of the graphs for Mr. Wright's class and Mr. Chu's class.

_____

_____

_____

_____

_____

2 Which graph does *not* include an outlier? Explain.

_____

_____

_____

Vocabulary

skewed a graph in which most of the data points are clustered near the lower values or the higher values.

cluster a group of data points that crowd near each other.

outlier a data point that is far away from other data points.

Solve.

Use the following situation for problems 3–6.

Joe asked some of his friends how many movies he or she watched last month. The table shows Joe's results.

Number of Movies Watched	1	2	3	4	5	6	7	8
Number of Friends	1	0	0	2	2	4	2	1

3 Graph the data points on a line plot.

4 List any outliers in the data. Explain why each value you list is an outlier.

_____

5 At what spinner number does a peak occur? _____

6 Describe the shape of the line plot.

_____

7 Write a problem in which data are collected and graphed and in which the data are skewed. Include a data table and a graph.

Name: _____

Compare Data Sets

**Study the example showing how to compare data sets.
Then solve problems 1–8.**

Example

Rob wanted to compare the effectiveness of two different brands of fertilizer, Maxi Growth and Sprout Up. He put Maxi Growth on one corn field and an equal amount of Sprout Up on another.

At the end of a month, he measured the height of 20 plants at random from each field. Rob made stacked dot plots and box plots. How can you use the graphs to compare the data?

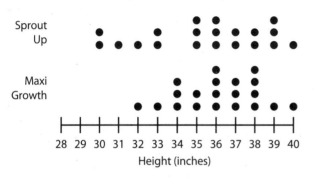

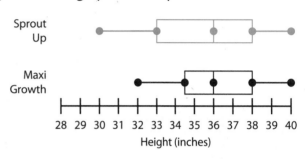

You can use the dot plot to find and compare the means and the box plot to find and compare the medians. You can also use the graphs to compare the variability of the data.

---

1 Find the mean of each brand and then compare the means and medians of the two brands.

_____

_____

2 Which brand has greater variability? Explain.

_____

_____

_____

3 Which fertilizer seems to be more effective? Explain.

_____

_____

_____

Lesson 29 Using Measures of Center and Variability to Compare Data

Solve. Use the following situation for problems 4–8.

Young High School and Valley High School are training for a
200-meter race. The average race times, in seconds, of the
top 9 sprinters for each school are shown in the table.

Valley High School	21.0	22.7	21.6	23.0	22.8	22.4	22.2	23.3	22.4
Young High School	22.6	23.1	23.4	22.5	22.8	22.4	21.9	23.0	23.2

4 Draw stacked dot plots of the data.

5 Draw stacked box plots of the data.

6 Calculate the mean for each school to the nearest tenth.

7 Which team seems more consistent? Explain.

_____

_____

8 Which team do you think is more likely to win? Use your
answers to problems 4–6 to explain your answer.
(Hint: A lower time indicates a faster speed.)

_____

_____

Name: _____

Using Measures of Center and Variability to Compare Data

Solve the problems.

1 Gina and Katrina measured the volume of water produced in several trials of a science experiment. The volumes that they measured are in the table.

Is one of the data values unlike the others?

Trial	1	2	3	4	5
Volume (cm³)	27	26	4	25	26

Is the mean or the median a better measure for a typical amount of water produced in the experiment? Explain.

_____

_____

2 Draw stacked dot plots that have the same shape and center but different spreads.

Are the dots on a dot plot with a large spread close together or far apart?

3 Donato lists his scores on this semester's math quizzes: 82, 94, 87, 98, 73, 77, 86, 87, 85, 84. What is the interquartile range of the data?

How do you calculate the interquartile range?

A 1.5   **C** 5

B 3.5   **D** 25

Jack chose **B** as the correct answer. How did he get that answer?

_____

_____

Solve.

Use this situation for problems 4–5.

The monthly average high temperatures in °F for Miami, FL are: 76, 78, 80, 83, 87, 89, 91, 91, 89, 86, 82, 78. The monthly average high temperatures in °F for Jacksonville, FL are: 65, 69, 74, 80, 87, 90, 92, 92, 88, 81, 74, 67.

4 Draw stacked box plots of the data.

Begin by arranging each set of data in order from least to greatest.

5 Compare the centers, ranges, and interquartile ranges of the data sets. What do they tell you about the temperatures of Miami and Jacksonville?

_____

_____

_____

_____

Which measure of center does a box plot show?

6 Tell whether each statement about the graph is *True* or *False*.

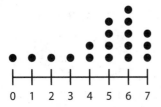

What is the shape of a symmetric distribution?

| | 0 1 2 3 4 5 6 7 | |

a. The graph is symmetric. ☐ True ☐ False

b. A peak occurs at 6. ☐ True ☐ False

c. The mean is 5. ☐ True ☐ False

Dear Family,

Your child is learning about probability concepts.

You can use words to describe the mathematical probability that an event will occur. Some words to describe probability are *certain, impossible, more likely than not, as likely as not,* and *less likely than likely.*

You can also use numbers between 0 and 1 to describe a probability. The diagram at the right shows both words and numbers that can be used to describe probability.

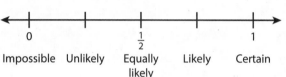

Consider the following example:

There are 12 marbles in a bag: 3 green, 3 red, and 6 blue. Mike reaches in and picks out 1 marble. Name outcomes that are *impossible, certain, as likely as not, more likely than not,* and *less likely than likely.* Use a number to describe each outcome.

On the next page you will see outcomes that your child might think of that have the given probabilities.

Vocabulary

probability the chance of an event happening.

event in mathematical terms, an experiment.

outcome one of the possible results of an event.

certain the probability of an event when that specific event will definitely happen.

impossible the probability of an event when that specific event will definitely not happen.

There are 12 marbles in a bag: 3 green, 3 red, and 6 blue. Mike reaches in and picks out 1 marble. Name outcomes that are *impossible, certain, as likely as not, more likely than not,* and *less likely than likely.* Use a number to describe each outcome.

Start by finding the total number of marbles. There are a total of 12 marbles. Use this to determine the outcomes.

Impossible: picking a yellow marble
There are no yellow marbles in the bag, so the probability of picking a yellow marble is 0.

Certain: picking a green, red, or blue marble
All of the marbles in the bag are either green, red, or blue; so the probability of picking a green, red, or blue marble is 1.

As likely as not: picking a blue marble
Half of the marbles in the bag are blue, so it is as likely as not likely that Mike will pick a blue marble. The probability of picking a blue marble is $\frac{1}{2}$.

More likely than not: picking a green or blue marble
More than half of the marbles are green or blue, so it is more likely than not likely that Mike will choose a marble that is either green or blue. The probability of picking a marble that is either green or blue is between $\frac{1}{2}$ and 1.

Less likely than likely: picking a red marble
Less than half of the marbles are red, so it is less likely than likely that Mike will choose a red marble. The probability of picking a red marble is between 0 and $\frac{1}{2}$.

Answer: You can use words or numbers to describe the probability of an outcome, so you can describe the probability of an event like picking 1 marble of a specific color out of a bag of 12 marbles using either words or a number from 0 and 1.

Understand
Probability Concepts

> Prerequisite: **How can you use benchmarks to compare fractions?**

Study the example showing how to use benchmarks to compare fractions. Then solve problems 1–7.

Example

Max lives $\frac{3}{10}$ of a mile from school. Chin lives $\frac{4}{5}$ of a mile from school. Who lives closer to school?

You can use a number line to compare the fractions.

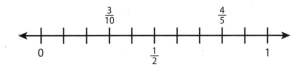

Compare the positions of $\frac{3}{10}$ and $\frac{4}{5}$ with the benchmark fraction $\frac{1}{2}$. You can see that $\frac{3}{10}$ is less than $\frac{1}{2}$, and $\frac{4}{5}$ is greater than $\frac{1}{2}$, so $\frac{3}{10} < \frac{4}{5}$. Max lives closer to school.

1 Use the benchmark fraction $\frac{1}{2}$ to compare $\frac{3}{8}$ and $\frac{3}{4}$.

a. Label $\frac{3}{8}$ and $\frac{3}{4}$ on the number line.

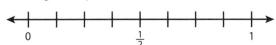

b. Compare $\frac{3}{8}$ and $\frac{3}{4}$ to $\frac{1}{2}$. Which is greater, $\frac{3}{8}$ or $\frac{3}{4}$? Explain.

_____

_____

2 How do you know the number of parts to divide a number line from 0 and 1 into when comparing fractions?

_____

_____

Vocabulary

benchmark fraction
a fraction that other fractions can easily be compared with.

Solve.

3 Compare $\frac{1}{8}$ and $\frac{5}{16}$ using the benchmark fraction $\frac{1}{4}$.

    a. Label $\frac{1}{8}$ and $\frac{5}{16}$ on the number line below.

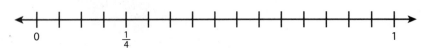

        0                     $\frac{1}{4}$ 1

    b. Use <, =, or > to compare $\frac{1}{8}$ and $\frac{5}{16}$. _____

    c. Explain how you compared the fractions.

    _____

4 Use a benchmark fraction to compare $\frac{2}{3}$ and $\frac{5}{6}$.

    a. Which benchmark fraction will you use? Why?

    _____

    b. Use <, =, or > to compare $\frac{2}{3}$ and $\frac{5}{6}$. _____

    c. Explain how you compared the fractions.

    _____

5 Explain how to use benchmarks to compare $\frac{9}{10}$ and $\frac{2}{7}$.

_____

6 Explain how to use benchmarks to compare $\frac{9}{10}$ and $\frac{13}{12}$.

_____

7 Anthony says that any two fractions that are the same distance away from a benchmark fraction are equal. Use any benchmark fraction and any two fractions to give an example that supports Anthony's statement. Then, use the same benchmark fraction and any two fractions that proves Anthony's statement is wrong.

_____

_____

Name: _____

Understanding Probability

Study the example showing the likelihood of certain events. Then solve problems 1–6.

Example

Sarah's playlist has 4 jazz songs, 10 hip-hop songs, 20 country songs, 6 blues songs, and 0 classical songs. She plays the songs at random on her device.

Find the probability that the next song will be jazz, hip-hop, country, blues, or classical. Then choose the point on the number line that best describes the probability.

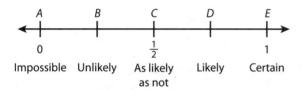

You can use the fact that there are 40 songs on Sarah's playlist and the given numbers of songs to find each probability. For example, there are 4 jazz songs and 40 songs, so the probability that a jazz song will play next is $\frac{1}{10}$, which makes it unlikely that a jazz song plays next.

Style of Music	Probability	Point
Jazz	unlikely	B
Hip-hop	unlikely	B
Country	as likely as not	C
Blues	unlikely	B
Classical	impossible	A

1 Why is it as likely as not that a country song will play next?

_____

2 Why is it impossible that a classical song will play next?

_____

3 Why is it unlikely that a hip-hop song will play next?

_____

_____

Vocabulary

probability the chance of an outcome or event occuring.

outcome one of the possible results in a situation or experiment.

Solve.

4 A baseball coach draws names to decide who will be the first player at bat. There are 5 girls and 10 boys on the team. Describe and explain the probability of each outcome.

a. The first batter is a girl.

_____

b. The first batter is a boy.

_____

5 A gym teacher has a box of tennis balls; 3 balls are green, 2 are red, and 4 are yellow. If you choose a ball without looking, which outcome is more likely, A or B? Complete the table.

Outcome A	Outcome B	More Likely (A or B)	Explanation
yellow ball	red ball		
green or red ball	yellow or red ball		
red or blue ball	purple ball		

6 Each student in your class tosses a coin. The result of each toss is either heads or tails.

a. Describe the probability that you get heads when you toss the coin. Explain.

_____

b. What part of the class would you expect to get heads? Explain.

_____

_____

c. What is the probability that everyone gets heads?

_____

_____

Name: _____

Reason and Write

Study the example. Underline two parts that you think make it a particularly good answer and a helpful example.

Example

Imagine a situation with an event that has at least six possible outcomes. Describe the situation and its possible outcomes. Include outcomes with the following probabilities:

- a certain outcome

- an impossible outcome

- an outcome that is as likely as not

- an outcome that is more likely than not

- an outcome that is unlikely

Show your work. Use words to describe the situation and its outcomes, and use a table to describe each event, its probability, and an explanation of how you found the probability.

Six students, Lisa, Carla, Sebastian, Sue, Nora, and Ann, run for class president. Each candidate is a possible outcome for the event of being voted class president.

Outcome	Probability	Explanation
A girl wins.	more likely than not	There are 6 candidates and 5 are girls.
Ann, Lisa, or Sebastian wins.	as likely as not	There are 6 candidates, so the chance that any of 3 will win is as likely as not.
One of the six students wins.	certain	Only the 6 students are running, so one must win.
A teacher wins.	impossible	A teacher cannot be voted class president.
A boy wins.	unlikely	There are 6 candidates and only 1 is a boy.

> Where does the example . . .
> - answer all parts of the problem?
> - use words to explain?
> - use a table to explain?

Solve the problem. Use what you learned from the model.

Imagine a situation with an event that has at least six possible outcomes. Describe the situation and its possible outcomes. Include outcomes with the following probabilities:

- a certain outcome

- an impossible outcome

- an outcome that is as likely as not

- an outcome that is more likely than not

- an outcome that is unlikely

Show your work. Use words to describe the situation and its outcomes, and use a table to describe each event, its probability, and an explanation of how you found the probability.

Did you ...
- answer all parts of the problem?
- use words to explain?
- use a table to explain?

Dear Family,

Your child is learning about experimental probability.

Experimental probability is the probability of an event happening based on actual results from an experiment, or trial. You can use the results from trials to predict the probability of an event occurring.

When you find an experimental probability, you compare the number of times a certain outcome occurs to the total number of trials in the experiment. For example, if you flip a coin 10 times and the coin lands on heads 4 times, then the experimental probability that the coin will land on heads is:

$$\frac{\text{number of times the coin landed on heads}}{\text{number of trials}} = \frac{4}{10}$$

Consider this situation:

George and Timmy are playing a game that uses a colored spinner. The spinner has four equal-size sections: red, yellow, green, and blue. George records the number of spins that land on each color. The results are shown in the table. Predict how many times the spinner will land on each color if George and Timmy spin the spinner 1,000 times.

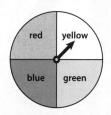

Color	Number of Spins
Red	20
Yellow	28
Green	30
Blue	22

The next page shows how your child can use experimental probabilities to solve this problem.

Vocabulary

trial what the experiment is called in probability.

experimental probability the probability of an event based on the results from an experiment.

NEXT →

George and Timmy are playing a game that uses a colored spinner. The spinner has four equal-size sections: red, yellow, green, and blue. George records the number of spins that land on each color. The results are shown in the table. Predict how many times the spinner will land on each color if George and Timmy spin the spinner 1,000 times.

Color	Number of Spins
Red	20
Yellow	28
Green	30
Blue	22

To find the experimental probability of landing on each color, first find the total number of spins in the experiment: $20 + 28 + 30 + 22 = 100$.

Probability of landing on red:

$P(\text{red}) = \dfrac{\text{number of red spins}}{\text{total number of spins}} = \dfrac{20}{100}$

Probability of landing on yellow:

$P(\text{yellow}) = \dfrac{\text{number of yellow spins}}{\text{total number of spins}} = \dfrac{28}{100}$

Probability of landing on green:

$P(\text{green}) = \dfrac{\text{number of green spins}}{\text{total number of spins}} = \dfrac{30}{100}$

Probability of landing on blue:

$P(\text{blue}) = \dfrac{\text{number of blue spins}}{\text{total number of spins}} = \dfrac{22}{100}$

Now that you've found the experimental probabilities of landing on each color, you can write and solve proportions to predict how many times you will land on each color if you spin the spinner 1,000 times. Find the number of times the spinner will land on red.

$$\dfrac{20}{100} = \dfrac{x}{1,000} \longrightarrow \dfrac{20 \times 10}{100 \times 10} = \dfrac{200}{1,000}, \text{ so } x = 200$$

This means you can predict the spinner will land on red 200 times if it is spun 1,000 times.

Similarly, you can predict the spinner will land on yellow 280 times, green 300 times, and blue 220 times if the spinner is spun 1,000 times.

Answer: This shows how you can use the results of the trial of 100 spins to write and solve proportions to predict the results for 1,000 spins. The proportions show that you can predict that the spinner will land on red 200 times, yellow 280 times, green 300 times, and blue 220 times if the spinner is spun 1,000 times.

Experimental Probability

Name: _____

Study the example showing how to describe the probability of an event. Then solve problems 1–11.

Example

Twelve tiles with the even numbers from 2 through 24 are placed in a bag. You draw a tile without looking.

You can describe the probability of various outcomes using words:

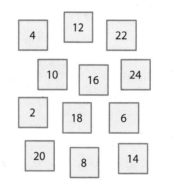

- Drawing an odd number is an impossible outcome.

- Drawing a numbered tile is a certain outcome.

- Drawing a prime number is unlikely.

- Drawing a number greater than 12 is as likely as not.

- Drawing a number greater than 6 is likely.

1 Why is drawing a number greater than 6 likely?

_____

2 Why is drawing a prime number unlikely?

_____

_____

Use the tiles from the example to classify each event as *impossible, unlikely, as likely as not, likely,* or *certain.*

3 Drawing a 4 or an 8. _____

4 Drawing a number less than 20. _____

5 Drawing a number less than 2. _____

6 Drawing a multiple of 2. _____

7 Drawing a number that is a factor of 24.

_____

Vocabulary

outcome one of the possible results in a situation or experiment.

event one or more possible outcomes.

probability the chance of an outcome or event occurring.

Solve.

8 Suppose you are playing a game using the spinner shown.

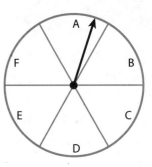

a. Name an outcome that is impossible.

_____

_____

b. Name an outcome that is certain.

_____

c. Name an outcome that is as likely as not.

_____

d. Name an outcome that is likely.

_____

9 At a pep rally, 95% of the fans are students and $\frac{1}{20}$ of the fans are teachers. The name of one fan is drawn at random. Whose name is more likely to be drawn, a teacher or a student? Use the number line to explain your answer.

_____

_____

10 The numbers shown describe the probabilities of various outcomes of an event. Show the probabilities on the number line and describe each probability in words.

$$\frac{8}{9} \qquad \frac{1}{2} \qquad \frac{3}{5} \qquad \frac{1}{10}$$

_____

11 Each face of a number cube has a different number from 1 to 6 on it. Dmitri rolls the number cube 5 times. Each time he rolls, the number 1 is on top. Dmitri says that if he rolls the cube again, he will most likely get a 1. Do you think that he is correct? Explain your answer.

_____

_____

Name: _____

Finding Experimental Probabilities

Study the example showing how to find experimental probabilities. Then solve problems 1–8.

Example

Nadine draws one colored cube at a time from a bag. She records the color of the cube before returning the cube to the bag. The table shows her results. Write the experimental probability of each color in words and with a ratio.

Color	Tally	Number of Times Drawn
red	|||	3
yellow	||||	4
blue	卌	5

From the table, you can see that Nadine drew from the bag a total of $3 + 4 + 5 = 12$ times.

$$P(\text{red}) = \frac{\text{number of red cubes}}{\text{number of draws}} = \frac{3}{12}, \text{ or } \frac{1}{4}$$

$$P(\text{yellow}) = \frac{\text{number of yellow cubes}}{\text{number of draws}} = \frac{4}{12}, \text{ or } \frac{1}{3}$$

$$P(\text{blue}) = \frac{\text{number of blue cubes}}{\text{number of draws}} = \frac{5}{12}$$

1 In the example above, why is the denominator of each ratio 12?

_____

2 Felipe repeats Nadine's experiment and has different results. Based on Felipe's experiment, what is the experimental probability of each color in words and with a ratio?

Color	Tally	Number of Times Drawn
red	||	2
yellow	|||	3
blue	卌 ||	7

$P(\text{red}) = $ _____

$P(\text{yellow}) = $ _____

$P(\text{blue}) = $ _____

3 Look at Nadine's and Felipe's results. Which color is there more of in the bag: red, yellow, or blue? How do you know?

_____

_____

_____

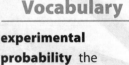

Vocabulary

experimental probability the probability of an outcome or event occurring based on the results of an experiment.

Solve.

4 A spinner is divided into equal sections that are numbered 1 through 5. Leon spins the spinner and records his results in a line plot, as shown. How many times did Leon spin the spinner?

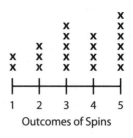

Outcomes of Spins

_____

5 Based on Leon's results in problem 4, find each probability.

P(1) = _____   P(2) = _____   P(3) = _____

P(4) = _____   P(5) = _____

6 Celia uses the same spinner that Leon used in problem 4. She spins the pointer 24 times and records her results in a tally chart. The last line of the chart was torn off by accident. According to her experiment, what is the probability that the spinner lands on 5? Explain.

_____

_____

_____

_____

Outcome	Tally
1	IIII
2	III
3	HHt II
4	HHt I

7 Combine Leon's results and Celia's results to find the experimental probability of spinning a 4.

_____

8 Use the results of problem 5 and problem 6. Find the sum of all the probabilities for Leon's experiment and for Celia's experiment. Compare the sums and explain the result.

Show your work.

Solution: _____

_____

Name: _____

Making Predictions Using Proportions

Study the example showing how probability can be used to make predictions. Then solve problems 1–6.

Example

Each person in Nadine's class draws a cube from a bag and records its color before returning it to the bag. The class repeats this experiment 240 times. The results are shown in the table. Predict the number of times a red cube will be drawn if the experiment is repeated 1,200 times.

Color	Times Chosen
red	83
yellow	78
blue	79

Based on 240 trials, $P(\text{red}) = \frac{83}{240}$. For 1,200 trials,

$P(\text{red}) = \frac{x}{1,200}$, where x represents the number of

times a red cube is drawn in 1,200 trials.

You can use a proportion to predict the number of times a red cube will be drawn in 1,200 trials:

$$\frac{x}{1,200} = \frac{83}{240}$$

1 Explain why the ratio $\frac{x}{1,200}$ equals the ratio $\frac{83}{240}$.

_____

2 Solve the proportion in the example to predict the number of times a red cube will be drawn in 1,200 trials.

Show your work.

Solution: _____

3 Write a proportion that could be used to predict the number of times a blue cube will be drawn in 500 trials.

_____

Lesson 31 Experimental Probability   **327**

Solve.

4 Devi conducts a poll about the election for mayor in her town. The current mayor is running against other candidates. She asks voters whether they plan to vote for the current mayor, against the current mayor, or if they are undecided. Her results are shown in the table. What is the experimental probability of each outcome?

Vote	Number of Voters
for	25
against	12
undecided	3

a. $P(\text{for}) = $ _____

b. $P(\text{against}) = $ _____

c. $P(\text{undecided}) = $ _____

5 Use the data in problem 4 to write and solve a proportion to predict the number of voters out of 1,000 that will have each response.

Show your work.

Solution: _____

_____

6 Alonso spins a spinner and gets a red outcome 12 times. He predicts that if he repeats the experiment 1,000 times, the pointer will stop on red 240 times. How many times did Alonso spin the spinner?

Show your work.

Solution: _____

Name: _____

Experimental Probability

Solve the problems.

1 Two months ago, a car dealership sold 150 cars. Thirty of the cars were red. Last month, the dealership sold 200 cars. Predict the number of red cars they sold last month.

Show your work.

What do you need to know in order to make a prediction?

Solution: _____

2 Carlotta rolls a number cube with faces labeled 1–6. Tell whether each statement is *True* or *False*.

When is an outcome likely?

a. Rolling a number less than 2 is unlikely. ☐ True ☐ False

b. Rolling a 4 or a 6 is likely. ☐ True ☐ False

c. Rolling an even number is as likely as rolling an odd number. ☐ True ☐ False

3 Ben spins a spinner with four sections labeled X, Y, W, and Z. He gets these results: X, X, X, Y, W, Z. What is the experimental probability that the spinner will *not* stop on Z on the next spin?

How many times did Ben spin the spinner? How many Zs did he spin?

A $\frac{1}{6}$ **C** $\frac{3}{4}$

B $\frac{1}{4}$ **D** $\frac{5}{6}$

Wayne chose **A** as the correct answer. How did he get that answer?

_____

_____

Solve.

4 Josh rolls a number cube with faces labeled 1–6 six times with these results:
3, 3, 5, 6, 1, 2
Elise spins the spinner shown six times with these results: ⊙, ⊙, ✧, ✕, ✧, ✧.
Hal flips a coin 6 times with these results:
H, T, T, T, H, T
Which of the following experimental probabilities are equal? Choose all that apply.

A Josh rolls an even number on the number cube.

B Elise spins the spinner and it lands on ✕.

C Hal flips the coin and it lands on H.

D Josh rolls a number less than 4 on the number cube

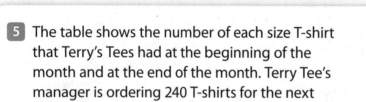
How do you calculate experimental probabilities?

5 The table shows the number of each size T-shirt that Terry's Tees had at the beginning of the month and at the end of the month. Terry Tee's manager is ordering 240 T-shirts for the next month. How many of each size shirt should the manager order?

Show your work.

Size	Beginning of Month	End of Month
S	60	20
M	75	10
L	40	10
XL	25	10
Total	200	50

How many T-shirts of each size were sold? How many T-shirts were sold in all?

Solution: _____

_____

Dear Family,

Your child is learning about probability models.

The *experimental probability* of an event occurring is based on actual results from an experiment. The *theoretical probability* of an event occurring is what you would expect to happen in an experiment.

Here's an example of each kind of probability.

- You would expect a coin to land on heads half the times that the coin is tossed. The theoretical probability of heads is $\frac{1}{2}$.

- You actually toss a coin 10 times and it lands on heads 7 times. The experimental probability of heads is $\frac{7}{10}$.

Experimental probability and theoretical probability do not always give the same results. However, the more trials you do in an experiment, the closer the experimental probability will be to the theoretical probability.

Consider the following example:

A family has two boys. The family tossed a coin to represent the likelihood of a boy if they have another child. They used heads to represent a boy and tails to represent a girl. The table below shows the results of their experiment. If the family has another child, predict whether the child will be a boy.

Coin Toss	Tally	Total
Heads (boy)	|||||		6
Tails (girl)	||||| ||||| ||||	14

On the next page you will see ways your child may find the experimental probability and the theoretical probability of whether the child will be a boy.

Lesson 32 Probability Models   **331**

NEXT

A family with two boys tossed a coin to represent the likelihood of a boy if they have another child. Heads represents a boy and tails represents a girl. The table below shows the results of their experiment. If the family has another child, predict whether the child will be a boy.

Coin Toss	Tally	Total
Heads (boy)	卌 I	6
Tails (girl)	卌 卌 IIII	14

Describe the sample space, or all of the possible outcomes for the experiment. There are two possible outcomes: the family will either have a boy or a girl. These outcomes are equally likely.

In this case you want to find the probability that the family has a boy. Compare the experimental probability to the theoretical probability.

Experimental probability of a boy:

$$P(\text{boy}) = \frac{\text{number of heads}}{\text{number of trials}} = \frac{6}{20}$$

The experimental probability of a boy is $\frac{6}{20}$, or $\frac{3}{10}$.

Theoretical probability of a boy:
Total number of possible outcomes: 2 (boy or girl)
Favorable outcomes: 1 (boy)

$$P(\text{boy}) = \frac{\text{number of favorable outcomes}}{\text{number of possible outcomes}} = \frac{1}{2}$$

The theoretical probability of a boy is $\frac{1}{2}$.

Answer: The experimental probability of having a boy is $\frac{3}{10}$ and the theoretical probability of having a boy is $\frac{1}{2}$. Based on the experimental probability, you would predict a boy only $\frac{3}{10}$ of the time. Based on the theoretical probability, you would predict a boy $\frac{1}{2}$ of the time.

Probability Models

Prerequisite: Predict an Outcome

Study the example showing how to use proportions to make predictions. Then solve problems 1–5.

Example

A class collected data on the types of vehicles parked in various parking lots near their school. They collected data on 250 vehicles. Use this data to predict how many of each type of vehicle there would be if they had collected data on 1,000 vehicles.

You can make a table and use proportions to predict the number of each type of vehicle there would be out of 1,000 vehicles.

Vehicle Type	Number	Probability Based on Data	Proportion	Prediction for 1,000 Vehicles
2-door cars	50	$\frac{50}{250}$	$\frac{50}{250} = \frac{x}{1,000}$	200
4-door cars	60	$\frac{60}{250}$	$\frac{60}{250} = \frac{x}{1,000}$	240
minivans	80	$\frac{80}{250}$	$\frac{80}{250} = \frac{x}{1,000}$	320
SUVs	32	$\frac{32}{250}$	$\frac{32}{250} = \frac{x}{1,000}$	128
trucks	28	$\frac{28}{250}$	$\frac{28}{250} = \frac{x}{1,000}$	112
Total	**250**			1,000

If the students had collected data on 1,000 vehicles, there would be 200 2-door cars, 240 4-door cars, 320 minivans, 128 SUVs, and 112 trucks.

1 Describe a method that may have been used to solve the proportions in the table.

_____

_____

_____

2 How can you check that your predictions are correct?

_____

_____

Vocabulary

experimental probability the probability of an outcome or event occurring based on the results of an experiment.

trial one of several identical experiments.

prediction a forecast of an outcome based on experimental results.

Solve.

3 A dog show has 6 small dogs, 12 medium-sized dogs, and 6 large dogs.

    a. What is the probability that a dog chosen at random is a small dog? Explain your reasoning.

    _____

    _____

    b. What is the probability that a dog chosen at random is *not* a large dog? Explain your reasoning.

    _____

    _____

4 Sam spins a spinner 24 times and gets the results shown in the table. If he were to spin the spinner 1,200 times, predict the number of times he would spin each color.

Show your work.

Color	Frequency
red	10
yellow	6
green	8

Solution: _____

5 Esperanza rolls a number cube and gets a six 8 times. Based on this experiment, she predicts that if she rolls the cube 1,600 times, she would get a six 640 times. How many times did she roll the number cube in her experiment? Explain your reasoning.

Show your work.

Solution: _____

Name: _____

Using a Probability Model

Study the example showing how a probability model can be used to predict an outcome. Then solve problems 1–7.

Example

Dave, Rachel, and Kira are going to be chosen at random in a drawing. A spinner with three equal sections, one for each student, is used to predict who will be chosen. The results of the experiment are shown in the table. Use the result to predict who will be chosen.

Outcome	Frequency
Dave	8
Kira	9
Rachel	7

The spinner in the experiment was spun 24 times. The experimental probabilities for each person are:

$P(\text{Dave}) = \frac{8}{24}$ $P(\text{Kira}) = \frac{9}{24}$ $P(\text{Rachel}) = \frac{7}{24}$

The individual with the greatest experimental probability is Kira, so you can predict that Kira will be chosen.

---

1 What is the sample space of this experiment?

_____

2 In this model, why is it important that the three sections of the spinner be the same size?

_____

_____

3 What is the theoretical probability that Kira will be chosen? Is it equal to the experimental probability?

_____

4 Will the theoretical probability always be different from the experimental probability? Explain.

_____

_____

Solve.

5 A computer game has two equally likely paths that a player can take. Path A has a favorable result, and Path B has an unfavorable result. You toss a coin to model the possible paths a player can take. Heads represents Path A and tails represents Path B. The results are shown in the tally chart.

Outcome	Tally
Heads (Path A)	卌 卌 IIII
Tails (Path B)	卌 卌

   a. What is the experimental probability that the path taken is Path A?

   _____

   b. What is the theoretical probability that the path taken is Path A?

   _____

   c. Why is the experimental probability different from the theoretical probability?

   _____

   _____

6 Refer to problem 5. Suppose the number of coin flips were increased to 200. How would this affect the experimental probability that the path taken is Path A?

_____

_____

7 A survey shows that at a certain intersection 50% of the traffic goes straight, 25% turns left, and 25% turns right. Describe a model for finding the probability that a randomly chosen car approaching that intersection continues straight ahead. Explain why you think your model is a good predictor for the outcomes at the intersection.

_____

_____

_____

_____

_____

Name: _____

Experimental and Theoretical Probabilities

**Study the example showing how to compare probabilities.
Then solve problems 1–6.**

Example

Kimi places 1 red, 1 blue, 1 black, and 1 green cube in a bag. She draws a cube without looking, records the outcome, and puts the cube back in the bag. Her results are shown in the table. Find and compare the experimental probability and the theoretical probability that the next cube Kimi draws will be red.

Kimi's Results

Outcome	Frequency
red	8
blue	4
black	7
green	5

The sample space is the same for both probabilities. The equally possible outcomes are red, blue, black, and green.

Theoretical probability: $P(\text{red}) = \dfrac{\text{number of favorable outcomes}}{\text{number of possible outcomes}} = \dfrac{1}{4}$

Experimental probability: $P(\text{red}) = \dfrac{\text{number of red cubes drawn}}{\text{total number of trials}} = \dfrac{8}{24}$

Because $\dfrac{1}{4} = \dfrac{6}{24}$ and $\dfrac{6}{24} < \dfrac{8}{24}$, the theoretical probability is less than the experimental probability.

---

1 The other students in Kimi's class conduct the same experiment. Their results are shown in the table. Do you expect the experimental probability of the class results to be closer to the theoretical probability than Kimi's results? Why?

Class Results

Outcome	Frequency
red	116
blue	121
black	124
green	119

_____

_____

_____

2 Compare the experimental probability from the class results with the theoretical probability. Are the class results closer to the theoretical probability than Kimi's results? Explain.

_____

_____

_____

Solve.

3 Heidi spins the spinner shown. She records her results in the line plot.

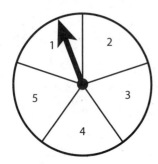

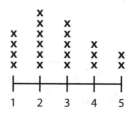

  a. What is the theoretical probability of each outcome?

_____

  b. What is the experimental probability of each outcome?

_____

4 Heidi's class conducts the same experiment and combines the results. Find the experimental probability based on the class results shown in the table. Record the probabilities in the table.

5 Compare the experimental probabilities from the class data to those from Heidi's data.

_____

_____

_____

_____

Outcome	Frequency	Experimental Probability
1	85	
2	80	
3	90	
4	75	
5	70	

6 Describe an event involving a number cube for which the experimental probability and the theoretical probability are both equal to $\frac{1}{3}$.

_____

_____

_____

Name: _____

Solve Problems with Experimental Probability

Study the example showing how to find experimental probabilities. Then solve problems 1–6.

Example

A floor is covered with black tiles and white tiles that alternate. Chau rolls marbles on the floor. Some stop on a white tile, some on a black tile, and some on a line between the tiles. Chau's results are shown in the table. What is the experimental probability of each outcome?

Outcome	Frequency
black tile	30
white tile	35
line between tiles	55

The experimental probabilities are:

$P(\text{black}) = \frac{30}{120}$ $P(\text{white}) = \frac{35}{120}$ $P(\text{line}) = \frac{55}{120}$

1　Do the outcomes appear to be equally likely? Explain.

_____

_____

2　What is the probability that a marble lands on a tile? Explain.

_____

3　Another 120 marbles are rolled on the floor. The combined results are shown in the table. Find the experimental probability of each outcome. Predict the outcome if another marble is rolled on the floor. Explain.

Outcome	Frequency
black tile	72
white tile	64
line between tiles	104

_____

_____

_____

4　Can you tell from the experiments how many tiles there are? Could you find the theoretical probabilities of landing on each color for this situation? Explain.

_____

_____

　　　　Lesson 32 Probability Models　**339**

Solve.

5 Chloe tracks the number of phone calls that she receives each day for one month.

Outcome (Number of Calls)	Frequency (Number of Days)
0	II
1	卌 I
2	卌 卌 II
3	卌
4	III
5	II

a. Do the outcomes appear to be equally likely? Explain.

_____

b. What is the experimental probability of each outcome?

_____

_____

c. Is it possible to find the theoretical probability using this data? Explain.

_____

d. Predict the number of phone calls that Chloe might expect to receive on the first day of the month following her experiment. Explain.

_____

_____

6 Suppose you want to design a spinner with outcomes that have the same probabilities as those in problem 5. What should be the measure of the angle for each section? Recall that there are 360° around the center of a circle. Number the sections of the spinner 0 through 5.

Show your work.

Solution: _____

_____

Name: _____

Probability Models

Solve the problems.

1 A tollbooth collector estimates that 85% of the vehicles that go through her tollbooth are cars and the other vehicles are not cars. She uses sixty random numbers from 00 to 99 to simulate the next sixty cars that will drive through her tollbooth.

There are 100 numbers from 00 to 99.

Which numbers could she have used to represent the two types of vehicles? What is the experimental probability that the next vehicle is not a car? Explain your answer.

89	03	86	75	55	41	96	97	38	33	79	91	22	20	24	39	75	08	48	29
96	09	89	19	69	77	24	70	06	34	12	91	73	94	57	21	10	72	23	57
97	50	04	39	49	58	12	19	02	10	76	44	51	15	98	71	03	75	26	47

_____

_____

_____

_____

2 You spin a spinner with 4 equal sections labeled A, A, B, C. Which statements are true? Select all that apply.

What are the theoretical probabilities of landing on each letter?

A The theoretical probability that you land on an A is twice the theoretical probability that you land on C.

B The theoretical probability that you land on B is $\frac{1}{4}$.

C The theoretical probability that you land on A is $\frac{1}{4}$.

D Every time you perform an experiment in which you spin the spinner 20 times, you will land on C exactly 5 times.

Solve.

3 A spinner, a number cube, and a coin are used to model an experiment. The spinner has four equal sections, labeled 1, 2, 2, and 3. The faces of the number cube are labeled 1, 1, 2, 2, 3, 3. On the coin, heads represents an even number and tails an odd number.

> What are the theoretical probabilities of getting an even or odd number with the spinner, cube, and coin?

Tell whether each statement is *True* or *False*.

a. *P*(even number) is the same with the spinner as with the cube. ☐ True ☐ False

b. *P*(even number) is the same with the coin as with the spinner. ☐ True ☐ False

c. *P*(odd number) is the same with the coin as with the spinner. ☐ True ☐ False

d. *P*(odd number) is the same with the coin as with the cube. ☐ True ☐ False

4 Josh tracked the number of text messages that he received in one week and the senders of those messages. He then did the same for one month. Use both sets of data to predict the number of text messages that Josh will receive from his family in 1 year. Then compare the predictions. Which prediction do you think is more accurate? Explain why.

Show your work.

Source of Text	1 Week	1 Month
family	13	60
friends	20	83
other	15	49

> Remember, there are 52 weeks in 1 year and 12 months in 1 year.

Solution: _____

_____

_____

_____

Dear Family,

> **Your child is learning about probability of compound events.**

A *compound event* is an event that consists of two or more events. You can describe the probability of a compound event occurring just as you can describe the probability of one event occurring.

Here are some examples of compound events that may be familiar to you.

- choosing a shirt and pants to wear
- choosing a dinner entrée and a dessert at a restaurant

In the restaurant example, suppose the menu has 4 entrées and 3 dessert items and a customer is equally likely to choose any combination of entrée and dessert. You can describe the probability of the customer choosing a certain combination. Knowing the probability might help a restaurant keep enough of each ingredient in stock.

Consider this situation:

A restaurant offers pizza in three sizes: small, medium, or large. For toppings, you can choose a vegetable mix, chicken, or both. You can also choose a thick or thin crust. If all the types of pizza are equally likely to be ordered, what is the probability that a customer will order a pizza that has only the vegetables mix and a thin crust?

The next page shows two ways your child may find the probability of a compound event.

Vocabulary

compound event   an event that consists of two or more simple events.

tree diagram   a visual model that shows all possible outcomes of an event.

A restaurant offers small, medium, or large pizzas. For toppings, you can choose a vegetable mix, chicken, or both. You can also choose a thick or thin crust. If all the types of pizza are equally likely to be ordered, what is the probability that a pizza with only the vegetable mix and a thin crust will be ordered?

One way:
Draw a tree diagram.

There are 18 possible combinations of pizza sizes, toppings, and crust.

For each size, there is 1 pizza with the vegetable mix only and thin crust. So there are 3 pizzas with only the vegetable mix and thin crust.

The probability that a customer will order a pizza that has only the vegetable mix and thin crust is $\frac{3}{18}$, or $\frac{1}{6}$.

Another way:
There are a total of 18 possible outcomes because you can choose from 3 sizes, 3 toppings, and 2 crusts: $3(3)(2) = 18$.

Identify and list favorable outcomes.

    small with vegetables and thin crust,
    medium with vegetables and thin crust,
    large with vegetables and thin crust

There are 3 favorable outcomes out of 18 possible outcomes.
The probability is $\frac{3}{18}$, or $\frac{1}{6}$.

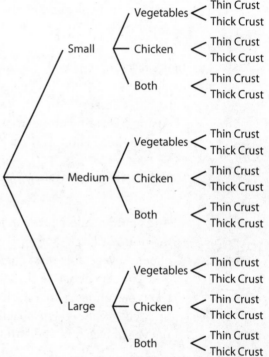

Answer: Both methods show that the probability is $\frac{1}{6}$, meaning that the probability a customer will order a pizza with only the vegetable mix and a thin crust is $\frac{1}{6}$.

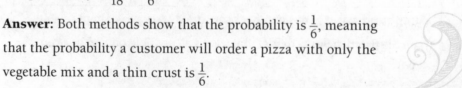

Probability of Compound Events

Name: _____

Study the example showing how to describe the sample space for an experiment. Then solve problems 1–8.

Example

Marcus and Bea play a game that involves rolling a number cube. Each face of the cube displays a different number from 1 through 6. Describe the sample space for this situation. What is the probability that the next roll of the cube results in an even number?

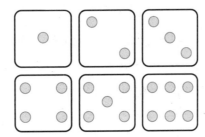

The sample space is the set of all possible outcomes. In this case, the sample space is {1, 2, 3, 4, 5, 6}. When all of the outcomes are equally likely, the theoretical probability of an event is the ratio of the number of favorable outcomes to the total number of outcomes.

There are 3 favorable outcomes for an even number: 2, 4, and 6. There are 6 possible outcomes.

$$P(\text{even}) = \frac{\text{number of favorable outcomes}}{\text{total number of outcomes}} = \frac{3}{6} = \frac{1}{2}$$

1 What is the theoretical probability of rolling a multiple of 3 in the example? Explain.

_____

2 What is the theoretical probability of rolling an 8 in the example? Explain.

_____

3 Describe two events that have the same probability using the sample space in the example.

_____

4 What is the sample space when you flip a coin? What is the theoretical probability of landing on heads?

_____

Vocabulary

sample space the set of possible outcomes for a situation or experiment.

theoretical probability the probability of an event or outcome occurring based on the possible outcomes in a same space.

Solve.

5 Trevon has 12 socks in a drawer. There are equal numbers of blue, black, and white socks. What is the sample space? Find the theoretical probability that a sock drawn at random out of the drawer is blue. Explain.

_____

_____

6 A bag contains 3 red marbles, 4 blue marbles, 5 purple marbles, and 6 white marbles.

a. Find the theoretical probability of drawing a marble of each color.

_____

_____

b. Jack performs an experiment and finds that the probability of drawing a purple marble is $\frac{1}{4}$. He concludes that the theoretical probability is incorrect. What is wrong with Jack's conclusion?

_____

_____

7 You toss a nickel and a dime. One outcome is heads for the nickel and tails for the dime: HT. What is the sample space for this experiment? What is the theoretical probability of getting at least 1 head? Explain.

_____

_____

8 Describe an experiment that has 12 possible outcomes. Then describe an event for that experiment that has a theoretical probability of $\frac{1}{4}$.

_____

_____

_____

Name: _____

Represent Sample Spaces and Identify Outcomes

Study the example showing how to represent sample spaces and identify outcomes. Then solve problems 1–4.

Example

Katie is playing a word game in which tiles with single letters on them are drawn from a bag. Toward the end of the game, the remaining tiles have the letters Z, A, I, L, A, and L. Katie draws two tiles at random. Find all of the ways in which Katie can draw two of the same letter.

You can make a table that lists all of the possibilities. Each listed pair is (first draw, second draw). There are 4 ways that Katie can draw two of the same letter.

Z, A	Z, I	Z, L	Z, A	Z, L
I, L	I, A	I, L	I, Z	I, A
L, A	L, L	L, Z	L, A	L, I
L, A	L, L	L, Z	L, A	L, I
A, L	A, Z	A, A	A, I	A, L
A, L	A, Z	A, A	A, I	A, L

1 You also can represent the sample space by using a tree diagram. The top letters are the first letter drawn. The lower letters are the second letter drawn. Complete the diagram.

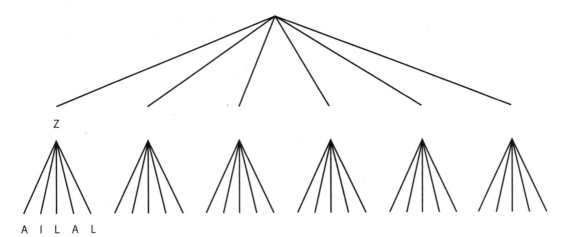

Z

A I L A L

2 Explain how to use the tree diagram to find all of the ways that Katie can draw two of the same letter.

_____

Solve.

3 Chico spins Spinner A and then spins Spinner B.

Spinner A

a. Make a table to show the possible outcomes. How many possible outcomes are there?

Spinner B

b. In how many ways can Chico get the same number both times?

_____

c. In how many ways can he get two odd numbers?

_____

4 Yolanda has three quarters. She tosses each quarter, one at a time.

a. Make a tree diagram to show the possible outcomes when she tosses the quarters, one at a time. How many possible outcomes are there?

b. In how many ways can Yolanda toss exactly two tails when she tosses the three quarters?

_____

c. In how many ways can Yolanda toss at least two tails when she tosses the three quarters?

_____

©Curriculum Associates, LLC   Copying is not permitted.

Name: _____

Probabilities of Compound Events

Study the example showing how to find probabilities of compound events. Then solve problems 1–6.

Example

Jeanne is playing a game with this spinner. She spins the pointer twice. What is the probability that the spinner lands on X exactly once?

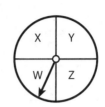

You can draw a tree diagram to understand the problem.

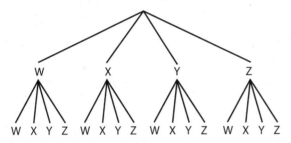

There are 16 possible outcome. List the outcomes where the spinner landed on X exactly once: WX, XW, XY, XZ, YX, ZX. There are 6 favorable outcomes. The probability that the spinner will land on X exactly once is $\frac{6}{16}$, or $\frac{3}{8}$.

1 List the outcomes in which the spinner lands on X at least once. _____

2 What is the probability that the spinner lands on X at least once? Explain.

_____

3 You can also use a table to help you. Complete the table. Use the table to find the probability that the spinner lands on Y exactly once. Explain.

	W	X	Y	Z
W		WX		
X				
Y				
Z				

Solve.

4 You can buy popcorn at the Village Theater in small, medium, or large sizes. The popcorn can be buttered or plain. If all of the choices are equally likely, what is the probability that a customer chooses a medium size with butter? Explain.

_____

_____

_____

5 Tommy plays a game in which he rolls two standard number cubes. On any one roll, what is the probability that the sum of the numbers rolled is an even number? Use a table to solve the problem.

Show your work.

Solution: _____

6 Jasmine creates a code formed by choosing two digits at random from 0 to 9. The digits can repeat.

a. How many possible two-digit codes can be formed?

_____

b. What is the probability that the sum of the two digits is 8? Explain.

_____

_____

_____

Name: _____

Find Compound Probability

Study the example showing how to find the probability of a compound event. Then solve problems 1–9.

Example

At the gift wrap counter of a store, a customer can choose white or silver gift wrap; a red, blue, or green bow; and a plain or decorated gift tag. If all of the possible choices are equally likely, what is the probability that a customer orders a gift with a red bow and a decorated gift tag?

You can use an organized table to identify the possible choices. Let W and S represent white and silver paper. Let R, B, and G represent red, blue, and green bows. Let P and D represent plain and decorated tags.

WRP	WBP	WGP
WRD	WBD	WGD
SRP	SBP	SGP
SRD	SBD	SGD

There are 12 possible outcomes. List the outcomes where a customer chooses a red bow and a decorated tag: WRD and SRD. There are 2 favorable outcomes. The probability that the a customer chooses a red bow and a decorated tag is $\frac{2}{12}$, or $\frac{1}{6}$.

---

1 Did you have to take the paper color into account when you found the probability in the example?

_____

2 What is the probability that a customer does NOT choose a red bow and a decorated tag? Explain.

_____

_____

_____

3 List the favorable outcomes if you want to find the probability that a customer chooses white wrapping paper and a plain tag.

_____

4 What is the probability that a customer chooses white wrapping paper and a plain gift tag? Show how you found your answer.

_____

Solve.

Use this situation for problems 5–8.

Daren sells sweatshirts in small, medium, and large sizes. The sweatshirts are sold both with and without hoods, and they are available in gray, red, and yellow.

5 Draw a tree diagram or make a table to represent the sample space. How many outcomes are possible?

6 How many of the possible sweatshirts are medium sweatshirts with hoods? Use your answer to find the probability that a randomly chosen sweatshirt is a medium with a hood.

_____

7 How many outcomes are sweatshirts with hoods? Use your answer to find the probability that a randomly chosen sweatshirt has a hood.

_____

8 Suppose you select a sweatshirt at random. What are two compound events that have a probability of $\frac{1}{9}$?

_____

_____

9 You spin the spinner shown three times. How many possible outcomes are there? What is the probability that the pointer stops on the letter A exactly two times? Explain.

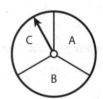

_____

_____

_____

Name: _____

Probability of Compound Events

Solve the problems.

1. Lamont is buying a new car. He needs to pick a color and an interior style. He can choose from white, black, and blue with either a fabric or leather interior. If Lamont chooses from all of the options at random, what is the probability that he will choose a black car?

What is the sample space for this situation?

A $\frac{4}{6}$ **B** $\frac{1}{6}$ **C** $\frac{1}{2}$ **D** $\frac{1}{3}$

2. You flip a coin three times. What is the probability of getting at least 1 head?

Can making a list, table, or tree diagram help?

A $\frac{1}{8}$ **B** $\frac{3}{8}$ **C** $\frac{7}{8}$ **D** 1

Leon chose **B** as the correct answer. How did he get that answer?

_____

3. Dai orders milk with her meal. The server asks her if she wants regular or chocolate. Dai can choose from skim, 2%, or whole, and from small, medium, or large. If all of the choices are equally likely to be ordered, what is the probability that Dai orders a regular, medium milk? Use a tree diagram to solve.

How can you use a tree diagram to determine favorable outcomes and all possible outcomes?

Show your work.

Solution: _____

Solve.

4 You form a two-digit whole number using the digits 1, 2, and 3. The digits can repeat. You want to find the probability that the first digit is less than the second digit. Tell whether each statement is *True* or *False*.

What are the favorable outcomes in this situation?

a. There are 6 possible outcomes. ☐ True ☐ False

b. The probability is $\frac{1}{3}$. ☐ True ☐ False

c. The number 23 is a favorable outcome. ☐ True ☐ False

5 Ming visited San Francisco (S), Dallas (D), and Lexington (L). In each city, she visited at least one of the following attractions: museum (M), ballpark (B), or concert hall (C).

How many possible outcomes are there for each city?

a. Make a table of all possible outcomes.

b. Based on the table, what is the probability that Ming went to a museum in Dallas? Explain.

_____

6 Ernest's favorite lunch is a turkey, lettuce, and tomato sandwich. Ernest can make the sandwich using either white bread or wheat bread. Sometimes he adds cheese, pickles, or mayonnaise in any combination, but other times he doesn't add anything. Ernest says that there are 8 different ways to make his favorite sandwich. Is he correct? Explain.

What can Ernest choose from to make his sandwich?

_____

_____

_____

_____

Name: _____

It's Probable

What you need: Recording Sheets, number cube (1–6), Symbol Cards

Directions

- Your goal is to score points by making correct predictions about events.

- Mix the symbol cards and place in a pile facedown.

- Player A rolls the number cube and records the number on the Recording Sheet. Then Player A picks a symbol card.

- Use the number and symbol to write the outcome in the Probability column. For example, if you get a 2 and the symbol $<$, write $P(< 2)$.

- Write the probability of the outcome, for example $P(< 2) = \frac{1}{6}$. Say the probability out loud. For example, "The probability of rolling a number less than 2 is $\frac{1}{6}$."

- Predict "yes" or "no" whether the event will occur on the next roll. Roll once again. Earn 1 point if your prediction is correct. Lose 1 point if it is incorrect.

- Players take turns. The player with the most points at the end of 10 rounds wins.

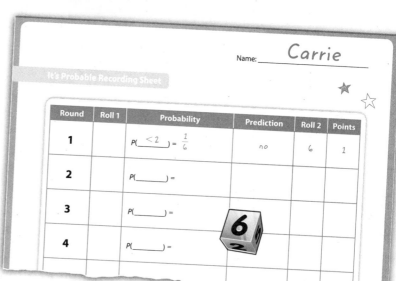

Name: **Carrie**

It's Probable Recording Sheet

Round	Roll 1	Probability	Prediction	Roll 2	Points
1		$P(\underline{< 2}) = \frac{1}{6}$	no	6	1
2		$P(\underline{\quad}) =$			
3		$P(\underline{\quad}) =$			
4		$P(\underline{\quad}) =$			

The closer the probability of an event occurring is to 1, the more likely it is to happen. If the probability of an event occurring is closer to 0, it is less likely to happen.

Name: _____

Round	Roll 1	Probability	Prediction	Roll 2	Points
1		P(_____) =			
2		P(_____) =			
3		P(_____) =			
4		P(_____) =			
5		P(_____) =			
6		P(_____) =			
7		P(_____) =			
8		P(_____) =			
9		P(_____) =			
10		P(_____) =			

It's Probable

Symbol Cards

<	>	=
<	>	=
<	>	=
<	>	=

Unit 5 Practice

Statistics and Probability

In this unit you learned to:	Lesson
identify random samples.	26
make statistical inferences from random samples.	27
compare data with measures of center and variability.	28, 29
find probabilities of single and compound events.	30, 31, 32, 33
compare theoretical and experimental probabilities.	31, 32

Use these skills to solve problems 1–6.

1 Which number best represents the probability that an outcome is unlikely to occur?

A 0

B $\frac{1}{10}$

C $\frac{1}{2}$

D $\frac{7}{8}$

2 A standard number cube is rolled and a coin is tossed. What is the probability of getting tails and an odd number?

A $\frac{1}{6}$

B $\frac{1}{4}$

C $\frac{1}{3}$

D $\frac{1}{2}$

3 Which sampling method or methods will produce a random sample of the students in your school? Select all that apply.

A Select every fifth student who enters the school.

B Choose the students on the boys' and girls' basketball teams.

C Ask for volunteers to take a survey.

D Assign each student a number and then select numbers at random.

4 There are 45 students on a field trip. Six students are chosen at random, five different times. The results are given.

2 boys and 4 girls

1 boy and 5 girls

2 boys and 4 girls

1 boy and 5 girls

3 boys and 3 girls

How many boys and girls do you think are on the field trip? Explain your answer.

_____

_____

_____

_____

Solve.

5 In baseball, a good hitter will get a hit 3 times out of every 10 times at bat. Vince ran an experiment in which a computer generated a random number from 00 to 99. He assigned the numbers 00 to 29 to represent a hit.

Part A: Is the experiment valid? Explain.

_____

Part B: After generating 200 random numbers, Vince counted 48 numbers from 00 to 29. Is this batter likely to be a good hitter? Explain.

_____

_____

6 The box plots show the results for two different classes on the same test. Select whether each statement is *True* or *False*.

Test Scores

a. The range for Class B is less than the range for Class A.　　□ True　　□ False

b. The mean and MAD can be determined from the box plot.　　□ True　　□ False

c. Class A likely has a higher MAD than Class B.　　□ True　　□ False

d. The interquartile range for Class B is greater than the interquartile range for Class A.　　□ True　　□ False

e. The median score for Class B is less than the median score for Class A.　　□ True　　□ False

Name: _____

Answer the questions and show all your work on separate paper.

Each week, Mr. Alvarez picks one student to lead the warm-up session in his gym class. There are 14 girls and 12 boys in the class. Mr. Alvarez writes each student's name on an index card and places the cards in a box. Then he picks a card from the box.

Mr. Alvarez wants to find the probability of selecting a boy and the probability of selecting a girl on the first week of class. Here is what he wants you to do.
- Describe the sample space.
- Find the theoretical probabilities of selecting a girl and of selecting a boy in the first week of class.
- Explain how you found these probabilities.

Mr. Alvarez also wants you to conduct an experiment.
- Use slips of paper and a paper bag.
- Write "G" on 14 slips and "B" on 12 slips to represent the boys and girls in the class.
- Pick a slip of paper from the bag and record the results.
- Put the slip of paper back in the bag, mix the slips, and pick another.
- Continue until you have recorded 50 selections.
- Calculate the experimental probability of picking a girl's name and of picking a boy's name.

Finally, compare the theoretical probabilities with the experimental probabilities. Tell how similar or how different the probabilities are and whether you got results that you expected.

Reflect on Mathematical Practices

After you complete the task, choose one of the following questions to answer.

1 **Model** What model did you use to record the data for the experiment? Why did you use this model?

2 **Reason Mathematically** How might you change the simulation to try to get less difference between the experimental and theoretical probabilities? Explain why.

> ## Checklist
>
> Did you . . .
> - [ ] organize your data for the experiment?
> - [ ] check your work?
> - [ ] explain your results using mathematical ideas?

Word Bank Here are some words that you might use in your answer.

experimental probability	sample space
theoretical probability	favorable outcome
uniform	non-uniform

Models Here are some models that you might use to find the solution.

Result	Tally
Boy	
Girl	

$$P(\text{boy}) = \frac{\text{number of times boy was selected}}{\text{total number of selections}}$$

Sentence Starters Here are some sentence starters that might help you explain your work.

The possible outcomes _____

A favorable outcome _____

To find the theoretical probability _____

Name: _____

My Examples

statistical question

a question that is expected to have variability in the data related to it

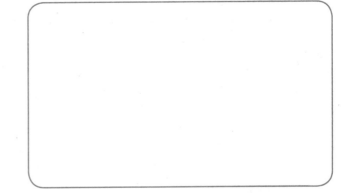

variability

the extent to which data are different from each other

random sample

sample in which every element in the population has an equal chance of being selected

biased sample

a sample that does not represent the whole population equally

population

the entire group considered for a survey

mean

the average of a data set; the sum of all the values divided by the number of values

median

the middle number in an ordered set of numbers when all the values are listed from least to greatest

mode

the most common number in a set of numbers

skewed

a graph in which most of the data points are clustered near the lower values or the higher values

cluster

a group of data points that crowd near each other

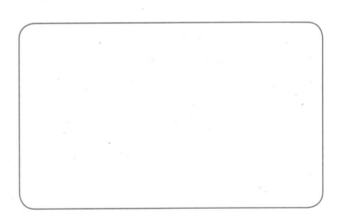

outlier

a data point that is far away from other data points

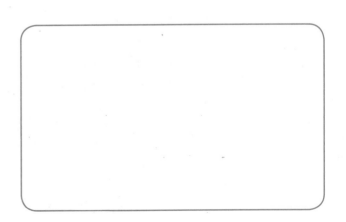

benchmark fraction

a fraction that other fractions can easily be compared with

My Examples

probability

the chance of an outcome or event occurring

outcome

one of the possible results in a situation or experiment

event

one or more possible outcomes.

experimental probability

the probability of an outcome or event occurring based on the results of an experiment

trial

one of several identical experiments

prediction

a forecast of an outcome based on experimental results

sample space

the set of possible outcomes for a situation or experiment

theoretical probability

the probability of an event or outcome occurring based on the possible outcomes in a sample space.

My Words

My Examples

Fluency Table of Contents

Addition and Subtraction with Rational Numbers—Skills Practice

Add integers.

1 $-5 + (-3) =$ _____

2 $14 + (-4) + 6 + (-16) =$ _____

3 $9 + (-4) =$ _____

4 $15 + (-7) + (-3) =$ _____

5 $-17 + 16 =$ _____

6 $-18 + (-17) =$ _____

7 $14 + (-16) =$ _____

8 $-16 + (-7) + (-4) =$ _____

9 $-19 + 36 =$ _____

10 $19 + 13 + (-9) =$ _____

11 $-17 + 14 + 7 + 10 =$ _____

12 $-12 + (-7) =$ _____

13 $-8 + 14 + (-2) + 6 =$ _____

14 $-17 + (-19) =$ _____

15 $79 + (-24) =$ _____

16 $23 + 14 + (-3) =$ _____

17 $-8 + 11 =$ _____

18 $-9 + 43 + (-11) =$ _____

19 $-6 + 12 + (-12) + 6 =$ _____

20 $16 + (-26) =$ _____

21 $45 + (-33) =$ _____

22 $18 + 19 + (-8) + (-19) + 7 =$ _____

23 $15 + (-3) + (-2) + 11 + 9 =$ _____

24 $7 + (-14) + (-6) + 13 + 4 =$ _____

Addition and Subtraction with Rational Numbers—Skills Practice

Name: _____

Add integers.

1 $-6 + (-4) =$ _____

2 $16 + (-8) + (-2) =$ _____

3 $17 + (-13) =$ _____

4 $13 + (-3) + 7 + (-17) =$ _____

5 $-13 + (-16) =$ _____

6 $-18 + 17 =$ _____

7 $15 + (-18) =$ _____

8 $-18 + (-9) + (-2) =$ _____

9 $-14 + 32 =$ _____

10 $18 + 16 + (-8) =$ _____

11 $-14 + 18 + 4 + 10 =$ _____

12 $-13 + (-4) =$ _____

13 $-16 + (-12) =$ _____

14 $-5 + 13 + (-5) + 7 =$ _____

15 $86 + (-12) =$ _____

16 $26 + 17 + (-6) =$ _____

17 $-4 + 12 =$ _____

18 $-2 + 64 + (-18) =$ _____

19 $-8 + (-2) =$ _____

20 $4 + (-5) + (-9) + 10 =$ _____

21 $-13 + (-13) =$ _____

22 $14 + 7 + (-4) + (-7) + 8 =$ _____

23 $16 + (-4) + (-2) + 17 + 13 =$ _____

24 $7 + (-14) + (-10) + 17 + 15 =$ _____

Addition and Subtraction with Rational Numbers—Skills Practice

Name: _____

Subtract integers.

1 $-8 - (-14) =$ _____

2 $-8 - 4 - (-8) =$ _____

3 $17 - (-8) =$ _____

4 $6 - (-7) - (-3) - 16 =$ _____

5 $-12 - 4 =$ _____

6 $-13 - (-7) =$ _____

7 $6 - (-3) =$ _____

8 $-5 - (-17) - (-5) =$ _____

9 $-62 - (-11) =$ _____

10 $-4 - 8 - 16 =$ _____

11 $-8 - 15 =$ _____

12 $4 - 17 - (-6) - 3 =$ _____

13 $11 - (-15) =$ _____

14 $-46 - 21 =$ _____

15 $41 - (-13) - 21 =$ _____

16 $14 - (-17) =$ _____

17 $55 - (-29) - (-45) =$ _____

18 $8 - (-14) - (-2) - 4 =$ _____

19 $6 - 7 - (-4) - 3 =$ _____

20 $-25 - 25 =$ _____

21 $30 - (-15) - 40 =$ _____

22 $-7 - (-14) - 4 - (-27) - 5 =$ _____

23 $-12 - (-7) - (-19) - (-13) - (-2) =$ _____

24 $-11 - (-5) - 9 - (-13) - (-5) =$ _____

25 $8 - (-3) - 10 - (-12) - (-7) =$ _____

Addition and Subtraction with Rational Numbers—Skills Practice

Subtract integers.

1 $-4 - (-19) =$ _____

2 $-7 - 9 - (-7) =$ _____

3 $18 - (-9) =$ _____

4 $-13 - 11 =$ _____

5 $8 - (-6) - (-4) - 18 =$ _____

6 $-16 - (-8) =$ _____

7 $2 - (-5) =$ _____

8 $-4 - (-18) - (-4) =$ _____

9 $-73 - (-11) =$ _____

10 $-3 - 6 - 17 =$ _____

11 $-7 - 14 =$ _____

12 $12 - (-13) =$ _____

13 $8 - 19 - (-2) - 1 =$ _____

14 $-41 - 38 =$ _____

15 $56 - (-17) - 46 =$ _____

16 $13 - (-19) =$ _____

17 $35 - (-31) - (-65) =$ _____

18 $18 - 3 - (-2) - 7 =$ _____

19 $12 - (-6) =$ _____

20 $-15 - 10 =$ _____

21 $14 - (-11) - 21 =$ _____

22 $-8 - (-16) - 6 - (-38) - 5 =$ _____

23 $-17 - (-19) - (-18) - (-1) - (-7) =$ _____

24 $-13 - (-12) - 15 - (-8) - 3 =$ _____

25 $-4 - (-8) - 4 - (-12) - 8 =$ _____

Add rational numbers.

1 $-7.25 + 8.67 =$ _____

2 $-\dfrac{5}{6} + 7 + \left(-\dfrac{1}{6}\right) =$ _____

3 $-5 + \dfrac{1}{4} =$ _____

4 $9 + (-10.2) =$ _____

5 $-\dfrac{1}{8} + \left(-\dfrac{7}{8}\right) =$ _____

6 $-\dfrac{5}{8} + \left(-\dfrac{1}{8}\right) + \dfrac{3}{4} =$ _____

7 $15.4 + (-16) =$ _____

8 $-1\dfrac{2}{5} + \dfrac{4}{5} =$ _____

9 $-8 + \left(-3\dfrac{1}{2}\right) =$ _____

10 $-18.04 + 7.9 =$ _____

11 $-11 + (-4.25) =$ _____

12 $-\dfrac{5}{6} + \left(-\dfrac{5}{6}\right) =$ _____

13 $\dfrac{2}{3} + \left(-\dfrac{1}{3}\right) =$ _____

14 $5.3 + (-16.4) =$ _____

15 $1\dfrac{3}{4} + \left(-\dfrac{1}{2}\right) + \left(-\dfrac{1}{4}\right) =$ _____

16 $-5.75 + 10 =$ _____

17 $-8.9 + (-7.2) + 18.9 =$ _____

18 $-4.2 + (-3.7) =$ _____

19 $3.5 + (-13.5) + (-5.6) =$ _____

20 $-3\dfrac{1}{6} + (-8) =$ _____

Addition and Subtraction with Rational Numbers—Skills Practice

Name: _____

Add rational numbers.

Form B

1 $-5.25 + 9.76 =$ _____

2 $-\frac{5}{8} + 11 + \left(-\frac{3}{8}\right) =$ _____

3 $-6 + \frac{3}{4} =$ _____

4 $6 + (-8.2) =$ _____

5 $-1\frac{3}{8} + \frac{5}{8} =$ _____

6 $-2\frac{1}{5} + \frac{3}{5} =$ _____

7 $14.9 + (-17) =$ _____

8 $-\frac{1}{3} + \left(-\frac{5}{6}\right) + 1\frac{1}{6} =$ _____

9 $-9 + \left(-1\frac{1}{2}\right) =$ _____

10 $-16.08 + 5.2 =$ _____

11 $-12 + (-6.75) =$ _____

12 $-\frac{3}{4} + \left(-\frac{3}{4}\right) =$ _____

13 $\frac{4}{5} + \left(-\frac{3}{5}\right) =$ _____

14 $3.6 + (-18.8) =$ _____

15 $2\frac{1}{2} + \left(-\frac{1}{8}\right) + \left(-\frac{3}{8}\right) =$ _____

16 $-4.25 + 10 =$ _____

17 $-9.1 + (-4.3) + 19.1 =$ _____

18 $-4.1 + (-2.8) =$ _____

19 $4.5 + (-8.2) + (-14.5) =$ _____

20 $-4\frac{1}{3} + (-7) =$ _____

Add and subtract rational numbers.

1 $4\frac{3}{4} - \left(-2\frac{1}{4}\right) =$ _____

2 $-16.5 - 11 =$ _____

3 $\frac{1}{5} - \left(-\frac{4}{5}\right) =$ _____

4 $7.75 - 14.25 =$ _____

5 $-8\frac{1}{3} - (-4) =$ _____

6 $-15.7 - (-16.2) =$ _____

7 $8.7 - (-5.2) =$ _____

8 $6\frac{5}{6} - 9\frac{1}{6} =$ _____

9 $6.2 - (-6.8) =$ _____

10 $11.92 - 4.5 =$ _____

11 $2\frac{1}{4} - 8\frac{1}{2} + 7\frac{3}{4} =$ _____

12 $4.2 - 17.6 + 5.8 =$ _____

13 $-12.6 + 4.2 - (-2.6) =$ _____

14 $-5\frac{2}{5} - 8\frac{4}{5} + 15\frac{2}{5} =$ _____

15 $-6.5 + 11 - (-6.5) =$ _____

16 $\frac{1}{6} - (-7) + 3 - \left(-\frac{5}{6}\right) =$ _____

17 $\frac{1}{4} - 1\frac{3}{4} + 2\frac{3}{4} - \left(-2\frac{3}{4}\right) =$ _____

18 $-6.1 - 6 - (-6.1) + 16 =$ _____

19 $1.25 - 2.75 - (-3.75) + (-7.25) =$ _____

20 $8\frac{1}{5} - \frac{3}{5} + \left(-\frac{4}{5}\right) - \left(-1\frac{2}{5}\right) =$ _____

Add and subtract rational numbers.

1 $5\frac{5}{8} - \left(-3\frac{3}{8}\right) =$ _____

2 $-14.5 - 8 =$ _____

3 $9.75 - 16.25 =$ _____

4 $\frac{1}{6} - \left(-\frac{5}{6}\right) =$ _____

5 $-6\frac{1}{4} - (-2) =$ _____

6 $-14.3 - (-17.1) =$ _____

7 $9.2 - (-8.6) =$ _____

8 $4\frac{2}{5} - 7\frac{1}{5} =$ _____

9 $4.7 - (-9.3) =$ _____

10 $9.84 - 8.5 =$ _____

11 $3\frac{5}{6} - 2\frac{1}{3} + 6\frac{1}{6} =$ _____

12 $6.7 - 19.2 + 3.3 =$ _____

13 $-13.4 + 3.9 - (-3.4) =$ _____

14 $-6\frac{1}{2} - 7\frac{1}{2} + 16\frac{1}{2} =$ _____

15 $-4.5 + 13 - (-4.5) =$ _____

16 $-4.1 - 8 - (-4.1) + 18 =$ _____

17 $\frac{2}{5} - 1\frac{3}{5} + 3\frac{3}{5} - \left(-3\frac{3}{5}\right) =$ _____

18 $\frac{1}{3} - (-8) + 2 - \left(-\frac{2}{3}\right) =$ _____

19 $9\frac{3}{8} - \frac{5}{8} + \left(-\frac{5}{8}\right) - \left(-1\frac{1}{4}\right) =$ _____

20 $4.25 - 16.75 - (-0.75) + (-3.25) =$ _____

Addition and Subtraction with Rational Numbers—Repeated Reasoning

Name: _____

Find patterns in adding integers.

Set A

1 $-6 + (-48) + 6 =$ _____

2 $-6 + (-148) + 6 =$ _____

3 $-16 + (-48) + 16 =$ _____

4 $-16 + (-148) + 16 =$ _____

5 $-26 + (-48) + 26 =$ _____

6 $-26 + (-148) + 26 =$ _____

7 $-36 + (-48) + 36 =$ _____

8 $-36 + (-148) + 36 =$ _____

Set B

1 $-6 + (-48) + 16 =$ _____   **2** $-16 + (-48) + 26 =$ _____   **3** $-26 + (-48) + 36 =$ _____

4 $-6 + (-148) + 16 =$ _____   **5** $-16 + (-148) + 26 =$ _____   **6** $-26 + (-148) + 36 =$ _____

7 $-16 + (-48) + 6 =$ _____   **8** $-26 + (-48) + 16 =$ _____   **9** $-36 + (-48) + 26 =$ _____

10 $-16 + (-148) + 6 =$ _____   **11** $-26 + (-148) + 16 =$ _____   **12** $-36 + (-148) + 26 =$ _____

Describe a pattern you see in one of the sets of problems above.

_____

_____

_____

Addition and Subtraction with Rational Numbers—Repeated Reasoning

Name: _____

Find patterns in subtracting integers.

Set A

1 −9 − 37 − (−9) = _____

2 −9 − 137 − (−9) = _____

3 −19 − 37 − (−19) = _____

4 −19 − 137 − (−19) = _____

5 −29 − 37 − (−29) = _____

6 −29 − 137 − (−29) = _____

7 −39 − 37 − (−39) = _____

8 −39 − 137 − (−39) = _____

Set B

1 −9 − 37 − (−19) = _____

2 −19 − 37 − (−29) = _____

3 −29 − 37 − (−39) = _____

4 −9 − 137 − (−19) = _____

5 −19 − 137 − (−29) = _____

6 −29 − 137 − (−39) = _____

7 −19 − 37 − (−9) = _____

8 −29 − 37 − (−19) = _____

9 −39 − 37 − (−29) = _____

10 −19 − 137 − (−9) = _____

11 −29 − 137 − (−19) = _____

12 −39 − 137 − (−29) = _____

Describe a pattern you see in one of the sets of problems above.

_____

_____

_____

Addition and Subtraction with Rational Numbers—Repeated Reasoning

Name: _____

Find patterns in adding rational numbers.

Set A

1 $-0.9 + 4.9 + (-4.0) =$ ____   **2** $-0.8 + 4.9 + (-4.0) =$ ____   **3** $-0.7 + 4.9 + (-4.0) =$ ____

4 $-0.6 + 4.9 + (-4.0) =$ ____   **5** $-0.5 + 4.9 + (-4.0) =$ ____   **6** $-0.4 + 4.9 + (-4.0) =$ ____

7 $-0.3 + 4.9 + (-4.0) =$ ____   **8** $-0.2 + 4.9 + (-4.0) =$ ____   **9** $-0.1 + 4.9 + (-4.0) =$ ____

Set B

1 $-0.9 + 5.9 + (-5.0) =$ ____   **2** $-0.9 + 5.8 + (-5.0) =$ ____   **3** $-0.9 + 5.7 + (-5.0) =$ ____

4 $-0.9 + 5.6 + (-5.0) =$ ____   **5** $-0.9 + 5.5 + (-5.0) =$ ____   **6** $-0.9 + 5.4 + (-5.0) =$ ____

7 $-0.9 + 5.3 + (-5.0) =$ ____   **8** $-0.9 + 5.2 + (-5.0) =$ ____   **9** $-0.9 + 5.1 + (-5.0) =$ ____

Describe a pattern you see in one of the sets of problems above.

_____

_____

_____

Addition and Subtraction with Rational Numbers—Repeated Reasoning

Name: _____

Find patterns in subtracting rational numbers.

Set A

1 $4 - 2 =$ _____

2 $2 - 4 =$ _____

3 $6 - 5 =$ _____

4 $5 - 6 =$ _____

5 $8 - 3 =$ _____

6 $3 - 8 =$ _____

7 $5 - 1.5 =$ _____

8 $1.5 - 5 =$ _____

9 $7 - 2.5 =$ _____

10 $2.5 - 7 =$ _____

11 $12 - 3.5 =$ _____

12 $3.5 - 12 =$ _____

Set B

1 $-3 - 4 =$ _____

2 $-2 - 4 =$ _____

3 $-1 - 4 =$ _____

4 $-4 - 3 =$ _____

5 $-4 - 2 =$ _____

6 $-4 - 1 =$ _____

7 $-13 - 0.5 =$ _____

8 $-12 - 0.5 =$ _____

9 $-11 - 0.5 =$ _____

10 $0.5 - 13 =$ _____

11 $0.5 - 12 =$ _____

12 $0.5 - 11 =$ _____

Describe a pattern you see in one of the sets of problems above.

_____

_____

_____

Multiply rational numbers.

1 $-\dfrac{3}{5} \times \left(-\dfrac{5}{8}\right) =$ _____

2 $2 \times (-5) \times 3 \times (-4) =$ _____

3 $-0.2 \times (-0.4) =$ _____

4 $-\dfrac{1}{6} \times \dfrac{5}{6} =$ _____

5 $-9 \times (-4) =$ _____

6 $-8 \times 7 =$ _____

7 $0.2 \times (-0.05) \times 0.3 =$ _____

8 $-0.6 \times 0.03 =$ _____

9 $6 \times (-6) =$ _____

10 $-\dfrac{1}{5} \times \dfrac{3}{5} \times \dfrac{4}{5} =$ _____

11 $-\dfrac{1}{4} \times \left(-\dfrac{3}{4}\right) =$ _____

12 $-0.5 \times 0.4 \times 0.3 =$ _____

13 $0.5 \times (-0.7) =$ _____

14 $-7 \times (-3) \times (-4) =$ _____

15 $-7 \times (-4) =$ _____

16 $\dfrac{1}{3} \times \left(-\dfrac{2}{3}\right) =$ _____

17 $5 \times (-8) =$ _____

18 $-2 \times -6 \times -3 =$ _____

19 $-10 \times 14 =$ _____

20 $-\dfrac{5}{8} \times \dfrac{2}{5} \times \left(-\dfrac{1}{4}\right) =$ _____

21 $100 \times (-9) =$ _____

22 $-\dfrac{1}{4} \times \dfrac{3}{2} \times \dfrac{1}{2} =$ _____

23 $-0.5 \times 0.1 \times (-0.2) \times (-0.4) =$ _____

24 $-\dfrac{1}{2} \times \dfrac{3}{2} \times \dfrac{5}{2} \times \left(-\dfrac{1}{2}\right) =$ _____

Multiplication and Division with Rational Numbers—Skills Practice

Name: _____

Multiply rational numbers.

Form B

1 $\frac{1}{4} \times \left(-\frac{3}{4}\right) =$ _____

2 $5 \times (-2) \times 6 \times (-3) =$ _____

3 $-0.3 \times (-0.2) =$ _____

4 $-\frac{1}{3} \times \frac{2}{3} =$ _____

5 $-3 \times (-8) =$ _____

6 $-9 \times 6 =$ _____

7 $0.3 \times (-0.05) \times 0.6 =$ _____

8 $-0.4 \times 0.04 =$ _____

9 $9 \times (-9) =$ _____

10 $-\frac{2}{5} \times \frac{1}{5} \times \frac{3}{5} =$ _____

11 $-\frac{7}{8} \times \left(-\frac{3}{8}\right) =$ _____

12 $-0.2 \times 0.4 \times 0.6 =$ _____

13 $0.9 \times (-0.5) =$ _____

14 $-2 \times (-4) \times (-8) =$ _____

15 $-7 \times (-3) =$ _____

16 $-16 \times 10 =$ _____

17 $-\frac{5}{6} \times \frac{2}{5} \times \left(-\frac{1}{8}\right) =$ _____

18 $100 \times (-7) =$ _____

19 $-5 \times (-7) =$ _____

20 $9 \times (-8) =$ _____

21 $-\frac{1}{5} \times \left(-\frac{1}{2}\right) =$ _____

22 $-0.4 \times 0.1 \times (-0.3) \times (-0.5) =$ _____

23 $-\frac{1}{2} \times \frac{3}{2} \times \left(-\frac{3}{2}\right) \times \left(-\frac{1}{2}\right) =$ _____

24 $0.5 \times -0.2 \times (-2) \times 5 =$ _____

Multiplication and Division with Rational Numbers—Skills Practice

Name: _____

Divide rational numbers.

1 $-\dfrac{1}{3} \div \left(-\dfrac{1}{6}\right) =$ _____

2 $56 \div (-8) =$ _____

3 $-3.6 \div 0.1 =$ _____

4 $-\dfrac{1}{2} \div \dfrac{1}{8} =$ _____

5 $-44 \div (-4) =$ _____

6 $-9.8 \div (-1) =$ _____

7 $\dfrac{1}{6} \div \left(-\dfrac{1}{6}\right) =$ _____

8 $6.4 \div (-2) =$ _____

9 $35 \div (-5) =$ _____

10 $-\dfrac{3}{4} \div \left(-\dfrac{1}{2}\right) =$ _____

11 $-90 \div 9 =$ _____

12 $\dfrac{2}{5} \div \left(-\dfrac{2}{3}\right) =$ _____

13 $-8.9 \div 10 =$ _____

14 $-36 \div (-3) =$ _____

15 $-24 \div (-0.2) =$ _____

16 $-\dfrac{5}{3} \div \dfrac{5}{6} =$ _____

17 $-100 \div (-50) =$ _____

18 $5.5 \div (-0.5) =$ _____

19 $\dfrac{1}{8} \div \left(-\dfrac{1}{5}\right) =$ _____

20 $-7.5 \div (-2.5) =$ _____

21 $-32 \div 4 =$ _____

22 $-3.6 \div 1.2 =$ _____

23 $-42 \div (-6) =$ _____

24 $-\dfrac{1}{3} \div \left(-\dfrac{1}{3}\right) =$ _____

Multiplication and Division with Rational Numbers—Skills Practice

Name: _____

Divide rational numbers.

1 $-32 \div 8 =$ _____

2 $-\dfrac{1}{4} \div \left(-\dfrac{1}{8}\right) =$ _____

3 $-4.8 \div 0.1 =$ _____

4 $-\dfrac{1}{2} \div \dfrac{1}{6} =$ _____

5 $\dfrac{1}{5} \div \left(-\dfrac{1}{5}\right) =$ _____

6 $-7.6 \div (-1) =$ _____

7 $-66 \div (-6) =$ _____

8 $8.2 \div (-2) =$ _____

9 $56 \div (-7) =$ _____

10 $-\dfrac{5}{6} \div \left(-\dfrac{1}{2}\right) =$ _____

11 $-48 \div (-4) =$ _____

12 $\dfrac{3}{8} \div \left(-\dfrac{3}{5}\right) =$ _____

13 $-5.4 \div 10 =$ _____

14 $-70 \div 7 =$ _____

15 $7.5 \div (-2.5) =$ _____

16 $-\dfrac{5}{2} \div \dfrac{5}{8} =$ _____

17 $-100 \div (-25) =$ _____

18 $2.5 \div (-0.5) =$ _____

19 $\dfrac{1}{5} \div \left(-\dfrac{1}{3}\right) =$ _____

20 $-39 \div (-0.3) =$ _____

21 $30 \div (-5) =$ _____

22 $3.2 \div (-8) =$ _____

23 $-4.8 \div 1.2 =$ _____

24 $\dfrac{1}{4} \div \left(-\dfrac{1}{5}\right) =$ _____

Write fractions as decimals.

1 $-\dfrac{4}{5} =$ _____

2 $-\dfrac{1}{2} =$ _____

3 $-\dfrac{5}{9} =$ _____

4 $-\dfrac{2}{3} =$ _____

5 $-\dfrac{2}{9} =$ _____

6 $\dfrac{2}{5} =$ _____

7 $\dfrac{9}{2} =$ _____

8 $\dfrac{5}{3} =$ _____

9 $-\dfrac{7}{5} =$ _____

10 $-\dfrac{1}{4} =$ _____

11 $-\dfrac{10}{9} =$ _____

12 $\dfrac{3}{2} =$ _____

13 $\dfrac{7}{2} =$ _____

14 $-\dfrac{8}{5} =$ _____

15 $\dfrac{5}{6} =$ _____

16 $-\dfrac{11}{4} =$ _____

17 $\dfrac{5}{12} =$ _____

18 $\dfrac{7}{6} =$ _____

19 $-\dfrac{5}{8} =$ _____

20 $\dfrac{5}{4} =$ _____

21 $\dfrac{9}{8} =$ _____

Expressing Rational Numbers as Decimals—Skills Practice

Name: _____

Write fractions as decimals.

1 $-\dfrac{1}{2} =$ _____

2 $\dfrac{3}{5} =$ _____

3 $-\dfrac{7}{9} =$ _____

4 $-\dfrac{1}{5} =$ _____

5 $-\dfrac{1}{3} =$ _____

6 $\dfrac{2}{9} =$ _____

7 $\dfrac{7}{3} =$ _____

8 $-\dfrac{9}{5} =$ _____

9 $-\dfrac{3}{4} =$ _____

10 $-\dfrac{9}{2} =$ _____

11 $-\dfrac{6}{5} =$ _____

12 $-\dfrac{7}{2} =$ _____

13 $-\dfrac{3}{2} =$ _____

14 $\dfrac{1}{6} =$ _____

15 $\dfrac{11}{9} =$ _____

16 $\dfrac{11}{6} =$ _____

17 $-\dfrac{9}{4} =$ _____

18 $-\dfrac{3}{8} =$ _____

19 $-\dfrac{9}{8} =$ _____

20 $\dfrac{7}{12} =$ _____

21 $\dfrac{7}{4} =$ _____

Expressing Rational Numbers as Decimals—Repeated Reasoning

Name: _____

Find patterns with repeating decimals. Write each fraction or fraction sum as a repeating decimal.

Set A

1 $\dfrac{1}{3} =$ _____

2 $\dfrac{2}{3} =$ _____

3 $\dfrac{4}{3} =$ _____

4 $\dfrac{5}{3} =$ _____

5 $\dfrac{7}{3} =$ _____

6 $\dfrac{8}{3} =$ _____

7 $\dfrac{10}{3} =$ _____

8 $\dfrac{11}{3} =$ _____

9 $\dfrac{13}{3} =$ _____

10 $\dfrac{14}{3} =$ _____

Set B

1 $\dfrac{1}{6} =$ _____

2 $\dfrac{2}{6} =$ _____

3 $\dfrac{3}{6} =$ _____

4 $\dfrac{1}{6} + \dfrac{3}{6} =$ _____

5 $\dfrac{2}{6} + \dfrac{2}{6} =$ _____

6 $\dfrac{4}{6} =$ _____

7 $\dfrac{2}{6} + \dfrac{3}{6} =$ _____

8 $\dfrac{1}{6} + \dfrac{4}{6} =$ _____

9 $\dfrac{5}{6} =$ _____

Describe a pattern you see in one of the sets of problems above.

_____

_____

_____

Expressing Rational Numbers as Decimals—Repeated Reasoning

Name: _____

Find more patterns with repeating decimals. Write each fraction as a decimal.

Set A

1 $\dfrac{1}{9} =$ _____

2 $\dfrac{2}{9} =$ _____

3 $\dfrac{3}{9} =$ _____

4 $\dfrac{4}{9} =$ _____

5 $\dfrac{5}{9} =$ _____

6 $\dfrac{6}{9} =$ _____

7 $\dfrac{10}{9} =$ _____

8 $\dfrac{11}{9} =$ _____

9 $\dfrac{12}{9} =$ _____

Set B

1 $\dfrac{1}{11} =$ _____

2 $\dfrac{2}{11} =$ _____

3 $\dfrac{3}{11} =$ _____

4 $\dfrac{4}{11} =$ _____

5 $\dfrac{5}{11} =$ _____

6 $\dfrac{6}{11} =$ _____

7 $\dfrac{7}{11} =$ _____

8 $\dfrac{8}{11} =$ _____

9 $\dfrac{9}{11} =$ _____

Describe a pattern you see in one of the sets of problems above.

_____

_____

_____

Name: _____

Write an equivalent expression without parentheses, and combine terms if possible.

1 $5x + 6x =$ _____

2 $6n - 3(2n - 5) =$ _____

3 $0.5(-12p - 4) =$ _____

4 $\frac{1}{4}y + \frac{3}{4}(y - 8) =$ _____

5 $4(x - 6) + 30 =$ _____

6 $-8\left(m + \frac{1}{4}\right) =$ _____

7 $-8x - 4x + 3x + 2 =$ _____

8 $4.5a + 7 + 3.5a + 2 =$ _____

9 $-4 + 7y - 3y - 5 =$ _____

10 $\frac{1}{6}(12n + 36) =$ _____

11 $3(y + 7) - 5y =$ _____

12 $9y - 4x + 3y + 4x =$ _____

13 $8(6a + 7) =$ _____

14 $\frac{1}{6}y + 6 - \frac{7}{6}y - 4 =$ _____

15 $\frac{3}{2}x - \frac{1}{2}(x + 4) =$ _____

16 $6 + 2x + 4(x + 5) =$ _____

17 $-8(x + 3) =$ _____

18 $3y + 3(y - 2.5) =$ _____

19 $9\left(-\frac{1}{3}m + 4\right) - 6m =$ _____

20 $6.25m + 9 + 3.75m - 12 =$ _____

Write an equivalent expression without parentheses, and combine terms if possible.

1 $7x + 6x =$ _____

2 $10n - 5(2n - 5) =$ _____

3 $\frac{5}{4}x - \frac{1}{4}(x + 12) =$ _____

4 $4 + 2x + 7(x + 2) =$ _____

5 $6(x - 7) + 50 =$ _____

6 $-6\left(m + \frac{1}{2}\right) =$ _____

7 $-3 + 8y - 6y - 4 =$ _____

8 $\frac{1}{4}y + 9 - \frac{5}{4}y - 2 =$ _____

9 $9(3a + 8) =$ _____

10 $\frac{1}{8}(16n + 24) =$ _____

11 $-7(x + 4) =$ _____

12 $2y + 3(y - 1.5) =$ _____

13 $-9x - 5x + 6x + 3 =$ _____

14 $2.5a + 5 + 4.5a + 3 =$ _____

15 $15\left(-\frac{1}{5}m + 2\right) - 4m =$ _____

16 $4.25m + 7 + 6.75m - 11 =$ _____

17 $7(y + 7) - 11y =$ _____

18 $8x - 2 - 5x + 2 =$ _____

19 $0.5(-16p - 6) =$ _____

20 $\frac{1}{5}y + \frac{4}{5}(y - 10) =$ _____

Name: _____

Use the distributive property to write the expression as a product.   **Form A**

1 $7x + 7 =$ _____

2 $6y + 14 - 8y =$ _____

3 $25x - 5 =$ _____

4 $16y + (-4) =$ _____

5 $4 - 8y =$ _____

6 $-8x - 16 =$ _____

7 $-11x - 44 =$ _____

8 $10 + 70x =$ _____

9 $10 - (-4y) =$ _____

10 $-2x + 12 - 4x =$ _____

11 $-25y + (-55) =$ _____

12 $20y - (-5) =$ _____

13 $-21x + 14 =$ _____

14 $18x - 33 =$ _____

15 $4y + 22 + 7y =$ _____

16 $-7 + (-21x) =$ _____

17 $6 + (-12y) =$ _____

18 $-5x + 33 + 16x =$ _____

19 $15y - 35 =$ _____

20 $-40y + 100 =$ _____

Using Properties of Operations— Skills Practice

Name: _____

Use the distributive property to write the expression as a product. **Form B**

1 $8x + 8 =$ _____

2 $8y + 20 - 12y =$ _____

3 $5y + 33 + 6y =$ _____

4 $-5x + 18 - 4x =$ _____

5 $6 - 18y =$ _____

6 $-9x - 18 =$ _____

7 $-9 + (-27x) =$ _____

8 $20 - (-6y) =$ _____

9 $-24x + 18 =$ _____

10 $16x - 44 =$ _____

11 $4 + (-16y) =$ _____

12 $3 + 39x =$ _____

13 $-4x + 28 + 11x =$ _____

14 $30y - (-6) =$ _____

15 $-11x - 66 =$ _____

16 $20 + 80x =$ _____

17 $25y - 45 =$ _____

18 $36x - 6 =$ _____

19 $-60y + 90 =$ _____

20 $24y + (-3) =$ _____

Two-Step Equations—Skills Practice

Solve equations of form $px + q = r$ with integers.

1 $6x + 6 = 0$

2 $-3x + 9 = 6$

3 $5x + 4 = -6$

4 $-275 = 25x - 50$

5 $90 = 20x - 10$

6 $46 = 3x + 19$

7 $-15x - 45 = -45$

8 $12x - 14 = -38$

9 $97 = 10x + 27$

10 $-6x - 13 = 35$

11 $-127 = -50x + 23$

12 $8x + 5 = -3$

13 $7x + 4 = -38$

14 $-4x - 52 = -152$

15 $-8 = -6x - 2$

16 $-25 = 10x - 25$

Two-Step Equations—Skills Practice

Name: _____

Solve equations of form $px + q = r$ with integers.

1 $-4x + 12 = 8$

2 $8x + 8 = 0$

3 $5x + 6 = -14$

4 $-250 = 25x - 75$

5 $30 = 20x - 10$

6 $38 = 3x + 17$

7 $11x - 16 = -49$

8 $-18x - 36 = -36$

9 $86 = 10x + 26$

10 $-8x - 11 = 45$

11 $-164 = -50x + 36$

12 $0 = 12x - 12$

13 $-12 = -9x - 3$

14 $9x + 7 = -2$

15 $-8x + 23 = 103$

16 $-6x + 53 = 5$

Two-Step Equations—Skills Practice

Name: _____

Solve equations of form $px + q = r$ with rational numbers.

1 $-3x + 6 = 9.9$

2 $8\frac{3}{5} = -4x + 5\frac{3}{5}$

3 $1.2x + 5.3 = 0.5$

4 $-\frac{1}{4}x + 6 = 10$

5 $7 = 11 - 0.2x$

6 $0.4x + 15 = 39.8$

7 $1\frac{3}{8} = \frac{1}{4}x + 1$

8 $\frac{2}{3}x - 4 = 36$

9 $\frac{1}{5} = \frac{7}{5} - \frac{1}{10}x$

10 $-8.2 = -7.1 + 11x$

11 $-13\frac{3}{4} = -\frac{7}{10}x + \frac{1}{4}$

12 $\frac{1}{8}x + \frac{3}{4} = \frac{1}{4}$

13 $-5.6x + 8.8 = 3.2$

14 $8x - 4\frac{2}{3} = 19\frac{1}{3}$

Name: _____

Solve equations of form $px + q = r$ with rational numbers.

Form B

1 $-4x + 8 = 12.8$

2 $3\frac{1}{6} = -5x + 1\frac{1}{6}$

3 $-35\frac{1}{4} = -\frac{9}{10}x + \frac{3}{4}$

4 $9 = 18 - 0.3x$

5 $-4.2x + 9.5 = 5.3$

6 $6x - 12\frac{1}{3} = 23\frac{2}{3}$

7 $-9.4 = -8.6 + 8x$

8 $\frac{1}{4}x + \frac{7}{8} = \frac{3}{8}$

9 $-0.25x - 8.5 = 2.5$

10 $-14.5 = 0.5x - 14.5$

11 $1\frac{5}{6} = \frac{1}{2}x + 1$

12 $\frac{3}{4}x - 6 = 54$

13 $0.2x + 21 = 49.6$

14 $0.1x + 4.75 = -1.5$

Solve equations of form $p(x + q) = r$ with integers.

1 $6(x + 4) = 36$

2 $21 = 7(x + 3)$

3 $56 = -8(x + 9)$

4 $2(x - 6) = -26$

5 $-4(x - 5) = -44$

6 $5(x + 4) = 35$

7 $-6(x - 12) = 48$

8 $-9 = -9(x + 4)$

9 $10(x - 15) = -70$

10 $-2(x - 13) = 18$

11 $-36 = 12(x + 7)$

12 $-7(x + 7) = 49$

13 $3(x - 6) = 24$

14 $-24 = 4(x - 6)$

15 $-11(x + 2) = -66$

16 $8(x - 14) = 64$

Name: _____

Solve equations of form $p(x + q) = r$ with integers.

Form B

1 $8(x + 4) = 32$

2 $24 = 4(x + 7)$

3 $-9(x + 5) = 54$

4 $-5(x - 6) = -15$

5 $-12 = -3(x - 7)$

6 $10(x + 15) = 40$

7 $2(x - 4) = 22$

8 $-7(x + 8) = -7$

9 $-11(x - 12) = -77$

10 $5(x - 16) = 45$

11 $25(x - 14) = -75$

12 $42 = -6(x + 9)$

13 $9(x + 8) = 63$

14 $-8(x + 8) = -48$

15 $-12 = 3(x - 4)$

16 $-2(x + 12) = 24$

Solve equations of form $p(x + q) = r$ with rational numbers. **Form A**

1 $-\frac{1}{8}(x + 6) = \frac{1}{8}$

2 $0.25(p + 8) = 2$

3 $-0.2(w - 6) = -4$

4 $\frac{2}{5}(y + 5) = \frac{4}{5}$

5 $-6.9 = 3(x + 4.6)$

6 $-25(p - 7) = -2.5$

7 $\frac{1}{3} = \frac{1}{6}(m - 9)$

8 $4.5 = 5(x + 3)$

9 $10(x - 24.2) = 50$

10 $\frac{1}{4}(n + 2) = -\frac{5}{2}$

11 $11(x - 0.4) = 44$

12 $20 = \frac{5}{6}(m + 8)$

13 $-\frac{1}{5}(y + 2) = 4$

14 $7.6 = 2(n + 5.7)$

Two-Step Equations—Skills Practice

Name: _____

Solve equations of form $p(x + q) = r$ with rational numbers.   **Form B**

1 $-\frac{1}{4}(x + 7) = \frac{1}{4}$

2 $-0.2(p - 4) = -2$

3 $0.5(w + 10) = 5$

4 $\frac{3}{8}(y + 9) = \frac{3}{4}$

5 $-8.4 = 4(x + 6.3)$

6 $-75(p - 6) = -7.5$

7 $\frac{1}{4} = \frac{1}{8}(m - 7)$

8 $3.5 = 5(x + 4)$

9 $10(x - 31.4) = 40$

10 $\frac{1}{6}(n + 5) = -\frac{4}{3}$

11 $11(x - 0.6) = 66$

12 $15 = \frac{3}{5}(m + 6)$

13 $-\frac{1}{4}(y + 5) = 3$

14 $9.4 = 2(n + 6.5)$

Find patterns in two-step equations of form $px + q = r$. Solve each equation.

Set A

1 $2x + 3 = 19; x =$ _____

2 $2x + 3 = 20; x =$ _____

3 $2x + 3 = 21; x =$ _____

4 $4x + 3 = 19; x =$ _____

5 $4x + 3 = 20; x =$ _____

6 $4x + 3 = 21; x =$ _____

7 $8x + 3 = 19; x =$ _____

8 $8x + 3 = 20; x =$ _____

9 $8x + 3 = 21; x =$ _____

Set B

1 $0.25x - 3 = 2; x =$ _____

2 $0.25x - 4 = 2; x =$ _____

3 $0.25x - 5 = 2; x =$ _____

4 $0.5x - 3 = 2; x =$ _____

5 $0.5x - 4 = 2; x =$ _____

6 $0.5x - 5 = 2; x =$ _____

7 $x - 3 = 2; x =$ _____

8 $x - 4 = 2; x =$ _____

9 $x - 5 = 2; x =$ _____

Describe a pattern you see in one of the sets of problems above.

_____

_____

_____

Two-Step Equations—Repeated Reasoning

Name: _____

Find patterns in two-step equations of form $p(x + q) = r$. Solve each equation.

Set A

1 $3(x + 3) = 30; x =$ _____

2 $3(x + 4) = 30; x =$ _____

3 $3(x + 5) = 30; x =$ _____

4 $3(x + 6) = 30; x =$ _____

5 $3(x + 7) = 30; x =$ _____

6 $3(x + 8) = 30; x =$ _____

7 $3(x + 9) = 30; x =$ _____

8 $3(x + 10) = 30; x =$ _____

9 $3(x + 11) = 30; x =$ _____

Set B

1 $3(x - 2) = 18; x =$ _____

2 $3(x - 3) = 18; x =$ _____

3 $3(x - 4) = 18; x =$ _____

4 $3(x - 5) = 18; x =$ _____

5 $3(x - 6) = 18; x =$ _____

6 $3(x - 7) = 18; x =$ _____

7 $3(x - 8) = 18; x =$ _____

8 $3(x - 9) = 18; x =$ _____

9 $3(x - 10) = 18; x =$ _____

Describe a pattern you see in one of the sets of problems above.

_____

_____

_____

Solve inequalities with integers.

1 $3(m - 4) < 27$

2 $-13 < 4x + 7$

3 $-2x + 7 < 19$

4 $-45 < 5(p - 2)$

5 $21 < -7(x - 2)$

6 $-9x + 10 > -8$

7 $42 > 6(m + 10)$

8 $10(n - 11) > -60$

9 $-97 < -11x - 9$

10 $25x - 9 < -109$

11 $36 < 12(w + 1)$

12 $-130 > 50x + 20$

13 $-8(x - 3) < -40$

14 $2x - 22 > -8$

15 $-35 < -5(x + 9)$

Two-Step Inequalities—Skills Practice

Solve inequalities with integers.

1 $12(w - 3) > 60$

2 $-5x + 15 > -30$

3 $-22 < 11x - 77$

4 $-75 > 25(m - 1)$

5 $-32 > -8(x - 7)$

6 $10x - 4 < -84$

7 $40 < 4(n + 14)$

8 $-7x - 3 < -45$

9 $9(y - 16) < -63$

10 $8 < -2(x - 3)$

11 $50x + 6 > -94$

12 $33 > 3(p + 7)$

13 $6 > 8x + 30$

14 $-11(x + 7) < -88$

15 $5x - 18 < 17$

Solve inequalities with rational numbers.

1 $0.5x + 0.3 < -0.7$

2 $\frac{1}{4}(m + 8) > \frac{1}{2}$

3 $4 < -0.2x + 7$

4 $-9 < -0.1(y - 5)$

5 $-\frac{5}{8}x + 6 < 5$

6 $-\frac{1}{6}(x - 24) < 4$

7 $1.2m + 6.3 < 1.5$

8 $0.5 < 0.25(p + 8)$

9 $2.5n - 4.5 < 0.5$

10 $-2\left(y - \frac{1}{4}\right) > -\frac{1}{2}$

11 $-\frac{1}{4}x + 2\frac{1}{4} < 2$

12 $0.8x + 0.6 < 0.6$

13 $-\frac{3}{4} > \frac{1}{8}(n + 24)$

14 $4 > -\frac{1}{2}x - 5$

Solve inequalities with rational numbers.

1 $0.2x + 0.4 < -0.6$

2 $\frac{1}{8}(m + 16) > \frac{1}{2}$

3 $-\frac{1}{10}(x - 20) > 2$

4 $-\frac{2}{3} > \frac{1}{6}(n + 12)$

5 $0.9x + 0.7 > 0.7$

6 $-\frac{3}{4}x + 7 < 6$

7 $8 > -\frac{1}{2}x - 3$

8 $2.5n - 5.5 < 2$

9 $-4\left(y - \frac{1}{8}\right) > -\frac{1}{2}$

10 $\frac{5}{6}x + 7 < 12$

11 $-4.9x + 2.7 < 7.6$

12 $-\frac{1}{5}x + 3\frac{1}{5} > 3$

13 $9.4 < 8x + 3.8$

14 $1.1m + 5.1 < 2.9$

Two-Step Inequalities—Repeated Reasoning

Find patterns in two-step inequalities. Solve each inequality.

Set A

1 $3(x + 1) > 6$; x _____

2 $-3(x + 1) > -6$; x _____

3 $3(x + 1) > 3$; x _____

4 $-3(x + 1) > -3$; x _____

5 $3(x + 1) > 0$; x _____

6 $-3(x + 1) > 0$; x _____

Set B

1 $4(x + 2) > 12$; x _____

2 $-4(x + 2) > -12$; x _____

3 $4(x + 3) > 12$; x _____

4 $-4(x + 3) > -12$; x _____

5 $4(x + 4) > 12$; x _____

6 $-4(x + 4) > -12$; x _____

Describe a pattern you see in one of the sets of problems above.

_____

_____

_____

_____

Find more patterns in two-step inequalities. Solve each inequality.

Set A

1 $2x + 2 > -4$; x _____

2 $-2x + 2 > -4$; x _____

3 $3x + 2 > -4$; x _____

4 $-3x + 2 > -4$; x _____

5 $4x + 2 > -4$; x _____

6 $-4x + 2 > -4$; x _____

Set B

1 $0.5x - 2 > -3$; x _____

2 $-0.5x - 2 > -3$; x _____

3 $0.5x - 3 > -3$; x _____

4 $-0.5x - 3 > -3$; x _____

5 $0.5x - 4 > -3$; x _____

6 $-0.5x - 4 > -3$; x _____

Describe a pattern you see in one of the sets of problems above.

_____

_____

_____